SRA
Connecting
Math Concepts

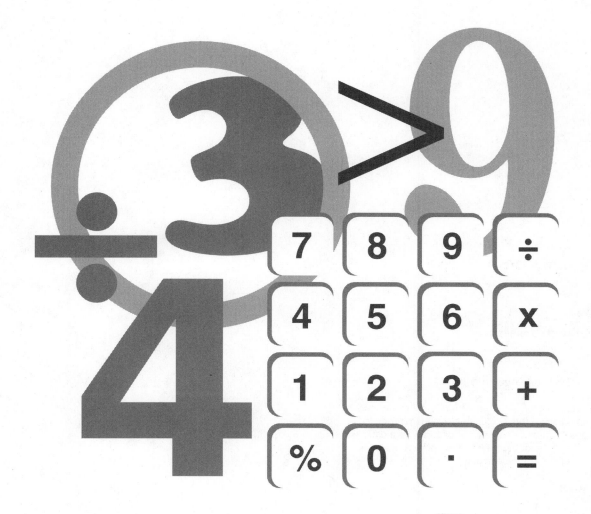

Columbus, Ohio

The McGraw·Hill Companies

www.sra4kids.com

Send all inquiries to:
SRA/McGraw-Hill
8787 Orion Place
Columbus, OH 43240-4027

Printed in the United States of America.

ISBN 0-02-684658-6

1 2 3 4 5 6 7 8 9 0 DBH 06 05 04 03 02

The **McGraw·Hill** Companies

Lesson 1

Part 1

5	10

Part 2

a. 8 4
x   2

b. 5 1
x   6

c. 5 2
x   4

d. 3 4
x   2

e. 7 1
x   5

Lesson 2

Part 1

a. 9 7
x   2

b. 4 6
x   5

c. 3 3
x   9

d. 4 8
x   2

e. 7 6
x   5

Part 2

a. 5 3 7
   − 2 9 7

b. 7 5 6
   − 5 4 7

c. 6 0 8
   − 2 9 6

d. 8 5 3
   − 2 8 0

Independent Work

Part 3 Write the numbers for counting by 5.

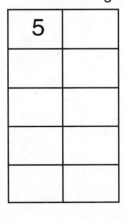

5	

Part 4 Write the answers.

a. 2 x 8 = ___   b. 5 x 3 = ___   c. 2 x 9 = ___

d. 9 x 5 = ___   e. 7 x 5 = ___   f. 9 x 3 = ___

g. 5 x 9 = ___

Part 5

a. 4 7 6
   + 4 0 1

b.   5 6
   + 8 0 9

c. 5 6 6
   − 3 2 5

d. 2 4 1
   + 9 9 9

1

Lesson 3

Part 1

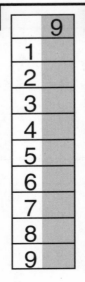
a.
b.
c.
d.

Part 2

a. 9 5
   x   4

b. 5 3
   x   5

c. 8 7
   x   2

d. 5 9
   x   3

Lesson 4

Part 1

a. $\frac{2}{3}$

b. $\frac{4}{1}$

c. $\frac{15}{12}$

d. $\frac{17}{20}$

e. $\frac{3}{15}$

f. $\frac{3}{2}$

g. $\frac{7}{4}$

h. $\frac{4}{7}$

i. $\frac{14}{7}$

Part 2

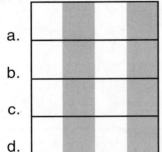
a.
b.
c.
d.

Lesson 5

Part 1

	9
1	
2	
3	
4	
5	
6	
7	
8	
9	

Part 2

a. 5 7
   x 2

b. 6 3
   x 2

c. 4 2
   x 5

d. 5 1
   x 3

e. 2 5
   x 9

Part 3

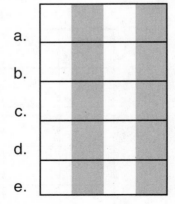
a.
b.
c.
d.
e.

a. $\dfrac{8}{3}$ b. $\dfrac{21}{15}$ c. $\dfrac{21}{50}$ d. $\dfrac{5}{8}$ e. $\dfrac{15}{18}$ f. $\dfrac{2}{1}$ g. $\dfrac{13}{30}$ h. $\dfrac{17}{13}$ i. $\dfrac{24}{13}$

Lesson 6

Part 1

a. $\begin{array}{r} 1\,3\,7 \\ \times\quad 2 \\ \hline \end{array}$ b. $\begin{array}{r} 5\,9 \\ \times\quad 3 \\ \hline \end{array}$ c. $\begin{array}{r} 6\,4\,1 \\ \times\quad 5 \\ \hline \end{array}$ d. $\begin{array}{r} 2\,5\,2 \\ \times\quad 4 \\ \hline \end{array}$

Part 2

	9
1	8
2	7
4	5
6	3
8	1
9	0

Part 3

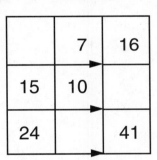

Lesson 7

Part 1

a. 8 x 9 = ___   b. 9 x 3 = ___   c. 9 x 5 = ___   d. 7 x 9 = ___

e. 4 x 9 = ___   f. 9 x 6 = ___   g. 9 x 9 = ___

a.

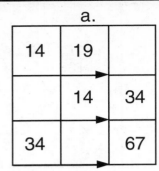

b.

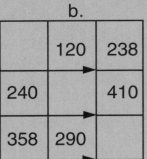

Lesson 8

| | Independent Work |

Part 1

a. 5 3 7
    x   5

b. 1 6 4
    x   5

c. 2 9 1
    x   3

d. 9 2 5
    x   3

Part 2 Write a column problem for each row. Figure out the missing numbers and write them in the table.

Remember, each row works like a number family. The small numbers on the arrow add up to the big number at the end of the arrow.

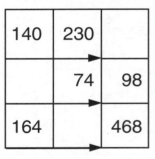

Lesson 9

Part 1

a. $8 \times 9 =$ ____

b. $0 \times 9 =$ ____

c. $9 \times 1 =$ ____

d. $9 \times 7 =$ ____

e. $5 \times 9 =$ ____

f. $5 \times 0 =$ ____

g. $0 \times 2 =$ ____

h. $1 \times 5 =$ ____

i. $1 \times 0 =$ ____

Part 2

	9
2	7
4	5
7	2
9	0

Part 3

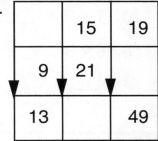

a.

	15	19
9	21	
13		49

b.

48	90	
17		57
	130	195

Part 4

a. $2 \times 9 =$ ____

b. $9 \times 6 =$ ____

c. $9 \times 4 =$ ____

d. $7 \times 9 =$ ____

e. $9 \times 3 =$ ____

f. $8 \times 9 =$ ____

g. $9 \times 5 =$ ____

h. $9 \times 9 =$ ____

Part 5

Write the missing numbers in the table.

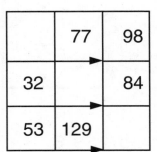

	77	98
32		84
53	129	

Test 1

a. 1 x 9 = ___   b. 5 x 9 = ___   c. 7 x 9 = ___   d. 4 x 9 = ___

e. 8 x 9 = ___   f. 3 x 9 = ___   g. 6 x 9 = ___   h. 0 x 9 = ___

i. 5 x 7 = ___   j. 5 x 5 = ___   k. 5 x 8 = ___   l. 5 x 4 = ___

Part 2

a.   b.   c.   d.

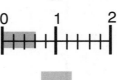

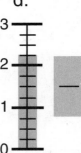

Part 3

a. 27 ——→ 139   b. | 56   c. | 12   d. —— 30 →70   f. | ——

                        ↓ 8   ↓   ↓ 156

                        ___   97   e. 132 471 ——→ ___   288

Part 4

a. 4 7 3   b. 5 1 8   c. 6 4 3
   – 2 6 7   – 3 4 9   –   6 3

Part 5

a. 3 8 2   b. 4 7 1   c. 3 7 8
   x   9   x   9   x   2

6

Lesson 11

Part 1

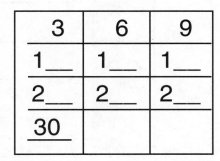

3	6	9
1__	1__	1__
2__	2__	2__
30		

Part 2

a.
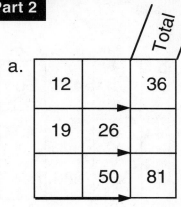

b.
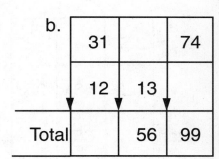

Lesson 12

Part 1

3	6	9
1__	1__	1__
2__	2__	2__
3__		

Part 2

a.
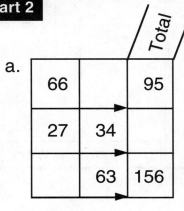

b.
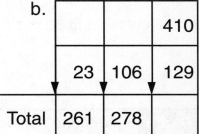

Lesson 13

Part 1

a.

307		427
422	531	953
Total	651	

b.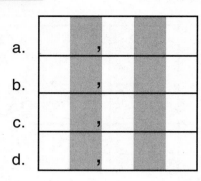

		479	604
200			407
325	686		

Part 2

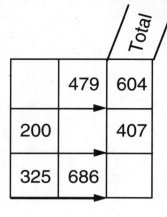

a.

b.

c.

d.

Part 3

a. 16 dollars and 12 cents _____

b. 31 dollars and 3 cents _____

c. 3 dollars and 31 cents _____

d. 140 dollars and 7 cents _____

e. 26 dollars and 80 cents _____

Part 4

____	____	____
____	____	____
____	____	____
____		

1	2	3
4	5	6
7	8	9
10		

Independent Work

Part 5   Write the numbers for counting by 9.

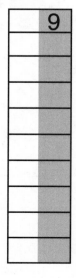

	9

Lesson 14

Part 1

a.		,	
b.		,	
c.		,	
d.		,	
e.		,	

Part 2

____	____	____
____	____	____
____	____	____
____		

1	2	3
4	5	6
7	8	9
10		

Part 3

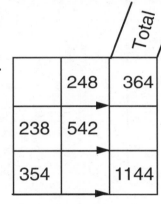

a.

		Total
	248	364
238	542	
354		1144

b.

243			549
	176	561	
Total		867	1286

Lesson 15

Part 1

a. $\begin{array}{r} 150 \\ \times\ \ \ 6 \\ \hline \end{array}$ b. $\begin{array}{r} 809 \\ \times\ \ \ 5 \\ \hline \end{array}$

c. $\begin{array}{r} 106 \\ \times\ \ \ 9 \\ \hline \end{array}$ d. $\begin{array}{r} 505 \\ \times\ \ \ 8 \\ \hline \end{array}$

Part 2

a. 14 thousand 6

b. 500 thousand 1

c. 341 thousand

d. 71 thousand 56

e. 8 thousand 90

f. 21 thousand 416

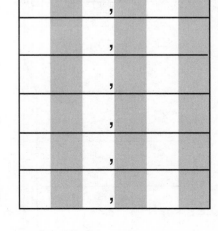

Lesson 16

Part 1

a. $\dfrac{12}{4} =$ b. $\dfrac{63}{9} =$ c. $\dfrac{15}{5} =$ d. $\dfrac{18}{3} =$ e. $\dfrac{30}{5} =$

Part 2

a. $\begin{array}{r} 8\,0\,4 \\ \times\quad 9 \\ \hline \end{array}$ b. $\begin{array}{r} 9\,0\,7 \\ \times\quad 9 \\ \hline \end{array}$ c. $\begin{array}{r} 3\,1\,0 \\ \times\quad 8 \\ \hline \end{array}$

Part 3

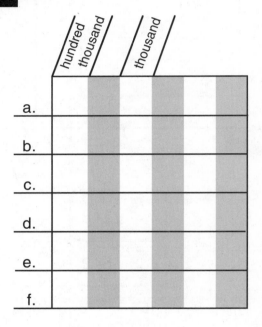

	hundred thousand		thousand			
a.						
b.						
c.						
d.						
e.						
f.						

Independent Work

Part 4

Complete the table.

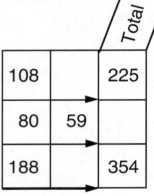

		Total
108		225
80	59	
188		354

Lesson 17

Part 1

a.

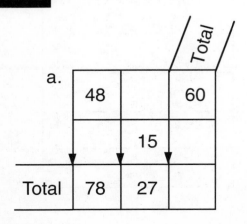

		Total
48		60
	15	
Total 78	27	

b.

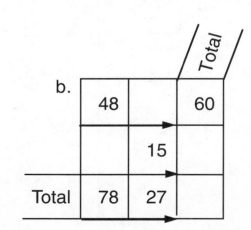

		Total
48		60
	15	
Total 78	27	

Part 2

a. $\dfrac{36}{4}$ =

b. $\dfrac{16}{8}$ =

c. $\dfrac{20}{4}$ =

d. $\dfrac{12}{3}$ =

e. $\dfrac{35}{5}$ =

Part 3

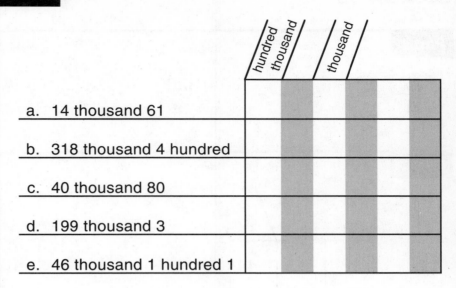

a. 14 thousand 61

b. 318 thousand 4 hundred

c. 40 thousand 80

d. 199 thousand 3

e. 46 thousand 1 hundred 1

Lesson 18

Part 1

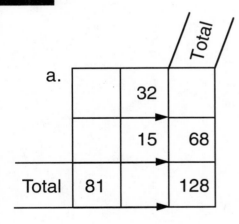 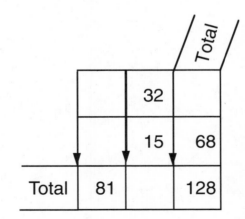

a.

Part 2

a. $\dfrac{8}{8}$ =   b. $\dfrac{8}{2}$ =   c. $\dfrac{8}{4}$ =   d. $\dfrac{21}{3}$ =   e. $\dfrac{15}{5}$ =   f. $\dfrac{2}{2}$ =

Lesson 19

a. $\dfrac{27}{9}$ =   b. $\dfrac{21}{3}$ =   c. $\dfrac{20}{4}$ =   d. $\dfrac{5}{5}$ =   e. $\dfrac{14}{2}$ =   f. $\dfrac{12}{3}$ =

Part 2

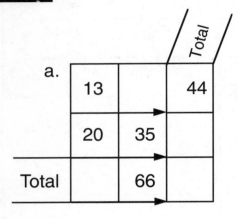

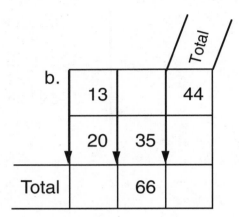

Test 2

Part 1

a. ▯—

b. ▯—

c. ▯—

d. ▯—

Part 2

a. _____

b. _____

c. _____

d. _____

e. _____

f. _____

g. _____

h. _____

1	2	3
4	5	6
7	8	9
10		

Part 3

	hundred thousand		thousand		
a.					
b.					
c.					
d.					

Part 4   Write the equation for each fraction that equals a whole number.

a. ▲▲△△

b. ▲▲▲▲

c. ⊕⊕⊕⊕

d. ●●●○

e. ⊛⊛⊛⊛

f.

Part 5   Find the area of each rectangle. Write the multiplication problem and the answer with the unit name.

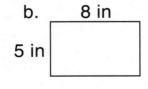

a. 4 ft
   36 ft

b. 8 in
   5 in

c. 16 mi
   2 mi

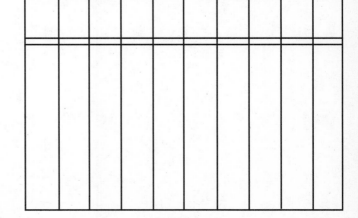

Write the answer to each problem.

a. 543
   − 149

c. 306
   x   5

Write the problem and answer for each column. Copy the missing numbers in the table.

b. 682
   − 593

d. 704
   x   9

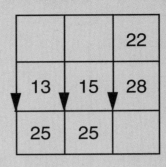

		22
13	15	28
25	25	

14

Lesson 21

a. 5 x = 40

b. 3 x = 21

c. 9 x = 18

d. 2 x ■ = 16

Part 2

a. 27 ___ 27

b. 207 ___ 27

c. 207 ___ 207

d. 14 ___ 41

e. 832 ___ 832

f. 1 ___ 0

Part 3

	hundred thousand		thousand		
a. 5 thousand 9 hundred					
b. 32 thousand 62					
c. 16 thousand 2 hundred 80					
d. 800 thousand 3 hundred 1					
e. 8 thousand 3 hundred 4					

Part 4

a.

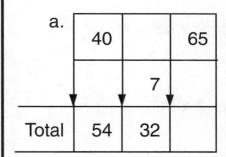

	40		65
		7	
Total	54	32	

b.

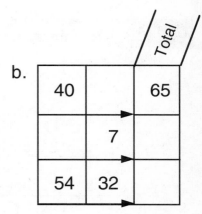

15

Lesson 22

Part 1

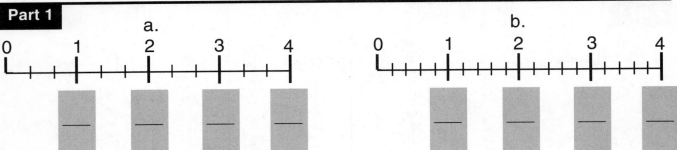

a.

b.

Part 2

a. 5 x ■ = 35

b. 3 x ■ = 6

c. 9 x ■ = 45

d. 2 x ■ = 8

Part 3

		Total
49	13	
18		
Total		64	131

Part 4

a. 77 __ 72

b. 0 __ 0

c. 1 __ 0

d. 100 __ 689

Independent Work

Part 5   Write the numeral for each description.

	hundred thousand		thousand		
a. 12 thousand 20					
b. 132 thousand 4					
c. 3 thousand 6 hundred 15					
d. 45 thousand 1 hundred 2					

16

Lesson 23

Part 1

a.
$$
\begin{array}{r}
7\,3,4\,0\,0 \\
\times \qquad 5 \\
\hline
\end{array}
$$

b.
$$
\begin{array}{r}
1\,2,3\,4\,5 \\
\times \qquad 2 \\
\hline
\end{array}
$$

Part 2

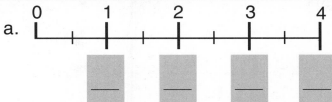

a.

b.

Part 3

		Total
	30	45
10		35
Total	25	

Part 4

Independent Work

Complete the sign.

a. 47 __ 46

b. 14 __ 14

c. 106 __ 160

d. 1603 __ 1630

Part 5

Write the symbols for each dollar-and-cents amount.

a. 13 dollars and 2 cents

b. 1 dollar and 19 cents

c. 134 dollars and no cents

d. 54 dollars and 1 cent

e. 100 dollars and 2 cents

Lesson 24

a. J is less than M.

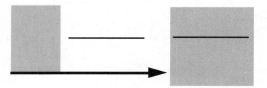

b. Rita is heavier than Paula.

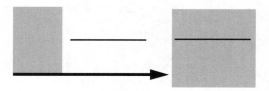

c. Peter is taller than Jan.

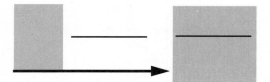

d. Wes is younger than Julie.

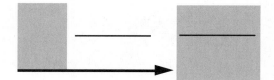

Part 2

a.

b.

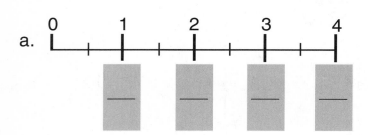

c.

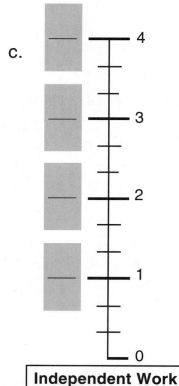

Independent Work

Part 3

a. 9 x ____ = 54

b. 9 x ____ = 36

c. 9 x ____ = 81

d. 9 x ____ = 63

e. 9 x ____ = 27

f. 9 x ____ = 45

g. 9 x ____ = 72

Part 4 Write the missing numbers.

a. 3 x ____ = 12

b. 5 x ____ = 20

c. 2 x ____ = 20

d. 9 x ____ = 27

e. 5 x ____ = 45

f. 5 x ____ = 10

g. 2 x ____ = 16

h. 2 x ____ = 14

Part 5 Write the missing sign.

a. 4 ▨ 4 = 0   d. 4 ▨ 1 = 4

b. 4 ▨ 1 = 5   e. 4 ▨ 1 = 3

c. 4 ▨ 0 = 0   f. 4 ▨ 4 = 16

Part 6

a.   4 3 7 9
    x   2

b.   1 2 3 4 5
    x   3

Lesson 25

Part 1

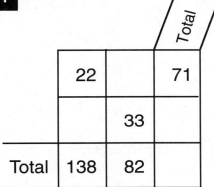

		Total
22		71
	33	
Total	138	82	

Part 2

a. 9 x ___ = 36   e. 9 x ___ = 27

b. 9 x ___ = 18   f. 9 x ___ = 81

c. 9 x ___ = 54   g. 9 x ___ = 63

d. 9 x ___ = 45   h. 9 x ___ = 72

Part 3

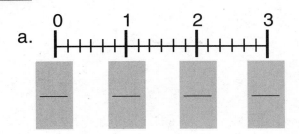

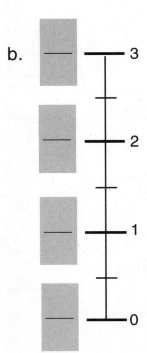

Part 4   Write the numeral for each description.

	hundred thousand		thousand		
a. 14 thousand 3 hundred					
b. 560 thousand 1 hundred					
c. 129 thousand 4 hundred 1					
d. 56 thousand 52					
e. 18 thousand 6 hundred 14					

Part 5   Write the sign to complete each equation.

a. 9 ▢ 9 = 0

b. 9 ▢ 9 = 81

c. 9 ▢ 9 = 18

d. 9 ▢ 1 = 8

e. 9 ▢ 1 = 9

f. 9 ▢ 1 = 10

g. 9 ▢ 0 = 9

Lesson 26

Part 1

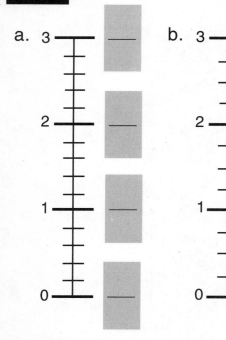

a. 3 ___
   2 ___
   1 ___
   0 ___

b. 3 ___
   2 ___
   1 ___
   0 ___

Part 2

a. ___ x 9 = 63   e. ___ x 9 = 27

b. ___ x 9 = 45   f. ___ x 9 = 18

c. 9 x ___ = 54   g. 9 x ___ = 72

d. 9 x ___ = 63   h. 9 x ___ = 36

Part 3 Complete the number maps.

3	___	___
___	___	18
___	___	___
30		

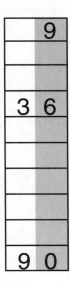

Lesson 27

Part 1

a. $\dfrac{6}{1}$ =

b. $\dfrac{3}{1}$ =

c. $\dfrac{1}{1}$ =

d. $\dfrac{18}{1}$ =

Part 2

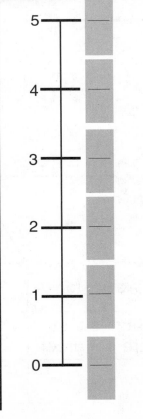

Part 3

	East coast	West coast	Total for both coasts
March		19	
April		22	35
Total for both months	31	41	

21

Lesson 28

a. $9\overline{)45}$ e. $3\overline{)6}$

b. $9\overline{)81}$ f. $2\overline{)10}$

c. $5\overline{)10}$ g. $9\overline{)36}$

d. $9\overline{)27}$ h. $9\overline{)54}$

Part 2

	Red birds	Blue birds	Total for both birds
Elm Street	64		
Maple Street	131	74	
Total for both streets		197	392

Independent Work

Part 3   Complete the sign to show $<$ or $>$.

a. 45 __ 60   b. 0 __ 1   c. 47,072 __ 46,700

Lesson 29

Part 1

4	__	__	__	__
__	__	__	__	__

1	2	3	4	5
6	7	8	9	10

Part 2

a. $3 = \dfrac{}{1} = \dfrac{}{2} = \dfrac{}{4} = \dfrac{}{6}$

b. $4 = \dfrac{}{1} = \dfrac{}{3} = \dfrac{}{5} = \dfrac{}{9}$

Part 3

	River Park	Hill Park	Total for both parks
Green stones	36		
Stones that are not green	196	221	
Total stones		307	539

Test 3

Part 1

a. _____

b. _____

c. _____

d. _____

e. _____

Part 2

		Total
	132	199
		357
Total	218	338	

Part 3

A wall is 47 feet wide and 9 feet tall. What is the area of the wall?

Part 4

a. $\dfrac{12}{5}$ b. $\dfrac{12}{3}$ c. $\dfrac{12}{9}$ d. $\dfrac{12}{2}$ e. $\dfrac{12}{10}$ f. $\dfrac{12}{1}$

Part 5

a. A pond had 45 sunfish. There was a total of 134 fish in the pond. How many were not sunfish?

b. 78 ducks were in the water, and the rest of them were on the shore. 189 ducks were on the shore. How many ducks were there in all?

Part 6

This table shows the number of boys and girls at two summer camps.

	Crooked Creek	Moody Meadow	Total for both camps
Boys	165	92	257
Girls	74	105	179
Total children	239	197	436

a. What's the total number of boys at both camps? _____

b. Which camp had more girls? _____

c. How many children were at Moody Meadow Camp? _____

d. Were there fewer boys or girls at Crooked Creek Camp? _____

23

Part 7

a. The snake was 13 inches longer than the worm. ————————————▶

b. Jan weighed 41 pounds less than Steve. ————————————▶

c. The tree was 18 feet taller than the house. ————————————▶

Lesson 31

Part 1

1	2	3	4	5
6	7	8	9	10

<table>
<tr><td>___
___</td><td>___
___</td><td>___
___</td><td>___
___</td><td>___
___</td></tr>
</table>

Part 2   Fill in the missing numbers.

			Total
		36	48
	40	15	
Total		51	

Part 3   Write the fraction for each whole number.

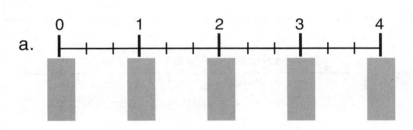

a.

0   1   2   3   4

b.

0   1   2   3   4

c. 4
    3
    2
    1
    0

Lesson 32

Part 1

a. 2 x 70 = ___   d. 4 x 60 = ___

b. 4 x 50 = ___   e. 8 x 20 = ___

c. 9 x 50 = ___   f. 3 x 90 = ___

Part 2

a. 5⟌3 5   b. 5⟌4 5

c. 5⟌1 5   d. 5⟌2 5

Part 3 Figure out the missing numbers. Then answer the questions in part 7 of your textbook.

This table is supposed to show the number of customers and workers at two different stores.

	Customers	Workers	Total people
Toy Palace		54	252
Sports and Sports	300		329
Total for both stores	498		

Lesson 33

Part 1

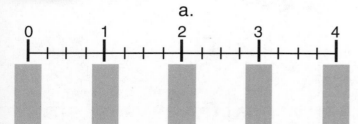

a. 2⟌6 2 8

b. 2⟌8 2 8

c. 2⟌6 4 2

Part 2 Figure out the missing numbers. Then answer the questions in part 6 of your textbook.

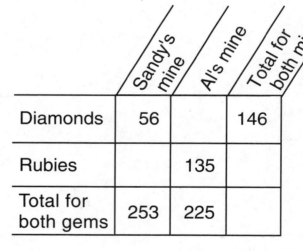

	Sandy's mine	Al's mine	Total for both mines
Diamonds	56		146
Rubies		135	
Total for both gems	253	225	

Part 3 Write the fractions for the whole numbers.

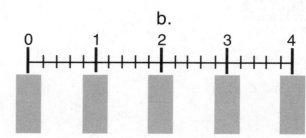

a.

0   1   2   3   4

b.

0   1   2   3   4

Lesson 34

Part 1

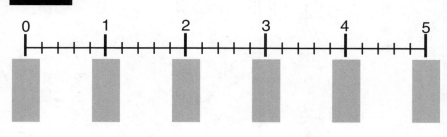

a. $4+\frac{1}{5}$ b. $1+\frac{3}{5}$

c. $2+\frac{2}{5}$ d. $0+\frac{4}{5}$

Part 2

a. $2\overline{)6}$ e. $3\overline{)0}$

b. $5\overline{)20}$ f. $6\overline{)6}$

c. $5\overline{)35}$ g. $1\overline{)6}$

d. $9\overline{)72}$ h. $9\overline{)45}$

Part 3

a. $2\overline{)684}$

b. $3\overline{)936}$

c. $2\overline{)628}$

Part 4

a. $\begin{array}{r} 4 \\ \times 20 \\ \hline \end{array}$ d. $\begin{array}{r} 3 \\ \times 70 \\ \hline \end{array}$

b. $\begin{array}{r} 3 \\ \times 20 \\ \hline \end{array}$ e. $\begin{array}{r} 3 \\ \times 40 \\ \hline \end{array}$

c. $\begin{array}{r} 2 \\ \times 70 \\ \hline \end{array}$ f. $\begin{array}{r} 9 \\ \times 40 \\ \hline \end{array}$

Lesson 35

Part 1

a. $4\overline{)480}$ b. $2\overline{)802}$ c. $3\overline{)60}$

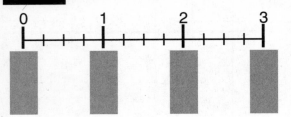

a. $2+\frac{1}{2}$

b. $2+\frac{1}{4}$

c. $1+\frac{1}{4}$

d. $0+\frac{1}{2}$

e. $2+\frac{3}{4}$

f. $1+\frac{1}{2}$

Part 3

a. $\begin{array}{r} 4 \\ \times\,5\,0 \\ \hline \end{array}$ d. $\begin{array}{r} 5 \\ \times\,9\,0 \\ \hline \end{array}$

b. $\begin{array}{r} 5 \\ \times\,8\,0 \\ \hline \end{array}$ e. $\begin{array}{r} 9 \\ \times\,8 \\ \hline \end{array}$

c. $\begin{array}{r} 5 \\ \times\,9 \\ \hline \end{array}$

Independent Work

Part 4   Figure out the missing numbers. Then answer the questions in part 4 of your textbook.

The table is supposed to show the number of cat fleas and dog fleas at two different places.

	Cat fleas	Dog fleas	All fleas
Al's Pet Shop	241		
Tim's Kennel	203	230	
Total for both places	444		838

Lesson 36

Part 1

a. $\begin{array}{r} 3\,4 \\ \times\,2\,0 \\ \hline \end{array}$ b. $\begin{array}{r} 4\,2 \\ \times\,3\,0 \\ \hline \end{array}$ c. $\begin{array}{r} 7\,8 \\ \times\,1\,0 \\ \hline \end{array}$ d. $\begin{array}{r} 6\,2 \\ \times\,4\,0 \\ \hline \end{array}$

Part 2

1	2	3
4	5	6
7	8	9
10		

a. $3\overline{)3}$ e. $3\overline{)0}$

b. $3\overline{)24}$ f. $3\overline{)21}$

c. $3\overline{)12}$ g. $3\overline{)18}$

d. $3\overline{)9}$ h. $3\overline{)27}$

Part 3

a. $2\overline{)1\underline{2}0}$ d. $2\overline{)1\underline{0}6}$

b. $2\overline{)1\underline{6}0}$ e. $2\overline{)\underline{2}06}$

c. $2\overline{)\underline{6}28}$ f. $4\overline{)1\underline{2}8}$

Part 4

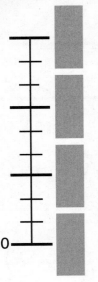 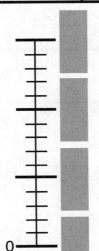

a. $2+\frac{3}{5}$ d. $1+\frac{4}{5}$

b. $0+\frac{1}{3}$ e. $2+\frac{1}{3}$

c. $2+\frac{2}{3}$ f. $2+\frac{2}{5}$

Lesson 37

Part 1

a. $5\overline{)15}$ e. $3\overline{)12}$ i. $5\overline{)30}$

b. $3\overline{)15}$ f. $2\overline{)12}$ j. $5\overline{)0}$

c. $2\overline{)18}$ g. $3\overline{)6}$

d. $3\overline{)18}$ h. $6\overline{)6}$

Part 2

a. $2\overline{)\underline{6}40}$ d. $2\overline{)1\underline{6}4}$

b. $3\overline{)\underline{2}76}$ e. $9\overline{)\underline{9}09}$

c. $5\overline{)\underline{2}05}$ f. $3\overline{)1\underline{8}9}$

Part 3

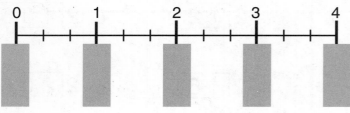

a. $1 + \frac{2}{3}$ d. $3 + \frac{1}{3}$

b. $3 + \frac{2}{4}$ e. $0 + \frac{3}{4}$

c. $2 + \frac{3}{4}$ f. $2 + \frac{2}{3}$

Lesson 38

Part 1

a. $3\overline{)186}$ b. $3\overline{)243}$ c. $3\overline{)606}$ d. $3\overline{)930}$ e. $3\overline{)129}$

Part 2

a. $4 + \frac{3}{5}$ b. $7 + \frac{1}{2}$ c. $4 + \frac{6}{9}$ d. $5 + \frac{4}{7}$

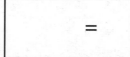   [=]   [ ]   [ ]

Part 3

a. 94	b. 63	c. 9	d. 94	e. 68
x 2	x 50	x 70	x 20	x 3

Independent Work

Part 4

a. 7	b. 3	c. 4	d. 3	e. 9	f. 8	g. 4	h. 7	i. 4	j. 3
x 4	x 4	x 8	x 6	x 4	x 3	x 6	x 3	x 4	x 3

Lesson 39

Part 1

a. $5 \overline{)400}$

b. $5 \overline{)50}$

c. $5 \overline{)355}$

d. $5 \overline{)105}$

Part 2

a. 46

b. 36

c. 39

d. 59

Part 3

a. $9 \overline{)27}$ d. $5 \overline{)15}$ g. $3 \overline{)21}$

b. $3 \overline{)27}$ e. $3 \overline{)6}$ h. $3 \overline{)12}$

c. $3 \overline{)15}$ f. $2 \overline{)6}$ i. $3 \overline{)24}$

Part 4

a. $\dfrac{}{2} = 6$

b. $\dfrac{}{4} = 5$

c. $\dfrac{}{8} = 9$

31

Test 4

Part 1

a. $5\overline{)35}$ g. $3\overline{)24}$

b. $5\overline{)15}$ h. $3\overline{)18}$

c. $5\overline{)40}$ i. $3\overline{)9}$

d. $5\overline{)25}$ j. $3\overline{)0}$

e. $5\overline{)45}$ k. $3\overline{)21}$

f. $5\overline{)30}$ l. $3\overline{)3}$

Part 4

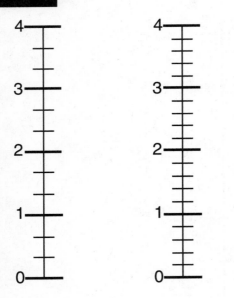

a. $3+\dfrac{4}{5}$ d. $3+\dfrac{1}{5}$

b. $1+\dfrac{2}{3}$ e. $0+\dfrac{1}{3}$

c. $3+\dfrac{1}{3}$

Part 2

a. $9 \times 4 =$ _____   e. $8 \times 4 =$ _____

b. $4 \times 4 =$ _____   f. $3 \times 4 =$ _____

c. $6 \times 4 =$ _____   g. $1 \times 4 =$ _____

d. $0 \times 4 =$ _____   h. $7 \times 4 =$ _____

Part 3

$$5 = \frac{}{1} = \frac{}{8} = \frac{}{6} = \frac{}{2}$$

Part 5

a. Jim buys the earmuffs and the boots. How much does Jim spend? _____

b. Tina buys the gloves, the boots and the cap. How much does Tina spend? _____

c. Jan buys the earmuffs, the gloves and the cap. How much does Jan spend? _____

a. 3)‾6‾0‾6‾   b. 3)‾2‾7‾6‾   c. 5)‾3‾5‾0‾   d. 2)‾4‾6‾0‾

a. 42	b. 5	c. 76	d. 37
x80	x60	x 4	x90

Lesson 41

Part 1

a.
```
  5 4
x 2 1
```

b.
```
  8 3
x 3 2
```

c.
```
  7 4
x 9 2
```

Part 2

a. 3) 2 1 6

b. 9) 1 8 0

c. 2) 8 0 4

d. 3) 6 9

Part 3   Write the answers.

a. 4 x 7 = ____

b. 3 x 3 = ____

c. 4 x 4 = ____

d. 8 x 4 = ____

e. 6 x 9 = ____

f. 6 x 4 = ____

g. 6 x 3 = ____

h. 9 x 4 = ____

Lesson 42

Part 1

Equivalent fractions are fractions that are equal.
They are equal if they have a shaded area that is
exactly the same size.

Problem 1

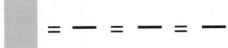

a. b. c. d. e.

= — = — = —

Problem 2

a. b. c. d. e.

 =

Part 2

a.
```
  8 4
x 1 2
```

b.
```
  2 3
x 5 2
```

Part 3

a. 3)216   b. 2)140

c. 2)68   d. 3)693

Part 4   Complete the fractions on each number line.

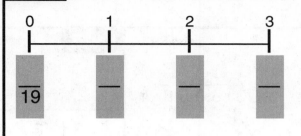

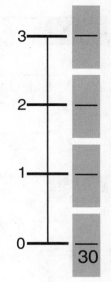

Lesson 43

Part 1

1	2	3	4	5
6	7	8	9	10

a. 4)36   b. 4)24   c. 4)16   d. 4)4

e. 4)28   f. 4)36   g. 4)8

Lesson 44

Part 1

a. 62
   x 53

b. 37
   x 41

c. 73
   x 93

Part 2

a. 4)32   b. 4)24   c. 4)12

d. 4)8   e. 4)28   f. 4)36

Part 3

a. 2)1204   b. 2)46   c. 5)1505   d. 3)27

Lesson 45

Part 1

a. $9\overline{)8100}$ b. $3\overline{)6060}$

c. $2\overline{)1860}$ d. $5\overline{)2505}$

Part 2

3	6	9
12	15	18
21	24	27
30		

a. $17 = 3 \times \underline{\hphantom{xx}} + \underline{\hphantom{xx}}$

b. $23 = 3 \times \underline{\hphantom{xx}} + \underline{\hphantom{xx}}$

c. $25 = 3 \times \underline{\hphantom{xx}} + \underline{\hphantom{xx}}$

d. $13 = 3 \times \underline{\hphantom{xx}} + \underline{\hphantom{xx}}$

e. $5 = 3 \times \underline{\hphantom{xx}} + \underline{\hphantom{xx}}$

f. $10 = 3 \times \underline{\hphantom{xx}} + \underline{\hphantom{xx}}$

Part 3

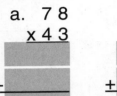

a. $\begin{array}{r} 78 \\ \times 43 \\ \hline \end{array}$ b. $\begin{array}{r} 54 \\ \times 36 \\ \hline \end{array}$ c. $\begin{array}{r} 37 \\ \times 49 \\ \hline \end{array}$

Part 4

a. $4\overline{)28}$ b. $4\overline{)16}$ c. $4\overline{)24}$ d. $4\overline{)36}$

e. $4\overline{)20}$ f. $4\overline{)32}$ g. $4\overline{)0}$ h. $4\overline{)4}$

Independent Work

Part 5   Write the letter and draw a line to show where each mixed number goes.

a. $3 + \dfrac{2}{3}$ b. $2 + \dfrac{3}{4}$

```
0       1       2       3       4
|+++|+++|+++|+++|+++|+++|+++|+++|
```

c. $0 + \dfrac{1}{3}$ d. $1 + \dfrac{2}{4}$

```
0       1       2       3       4
|++|++|++|++|++|++|++|++|
```

36

Lesson 46

Part 1

5	10
15	20
25	30
35	40
45	50

a. 13 = 5 x ___ + ___

b. 24 = 5 x ___ + ___

c. 33 = 5 x ___ + ___

d. 6 = 5 x ___ + ___

e. 47 = 5 x ___ + ___

f. 19 = 5 x ___ + ___

Part 2

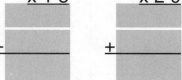

a. 5 7
   x 9 3

b. 2 8
   x 1 5

c. 6 8
   x 2 9

Part 3

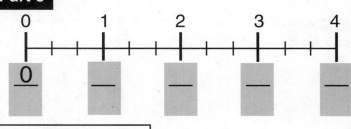

Independent Work

Part 4

a. 30 = 5 ▢ 6

b. 40 = 42 ▢ 2

c. 19 = 4 ▢ 15

d. 45 = 40 ▢ 5

e. 45 = 9 ▢ 5

f. 45 = 50 ▢ 5

Part 5

Write the fraction for each whole number. Write the letter to show where each mixed number goes on the number line.

a. $2 + \frac{3}{11}$

b. $4 + \frac{5}{11}$

c. $0 + \frac{9}{11}$

Lesson 47

3	6	9
12	15	18
21	24	27
30		

a. 17 = 3 x _____ + _____

b. 14 = 3 x _____ + _____

c. 29 = 3 x _____ + _____

d. 25 = 3 x _____ + _____

e. 10 = 3 x _____ + _____

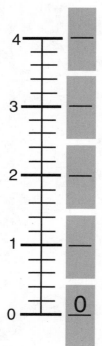

Part 2

a. 8 9
   x 2 3

b. 5 7
   x 4 3

c. 6 4
   x 3 5

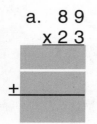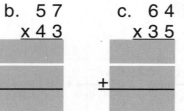

+ _____   + _____   + _____

Part 3

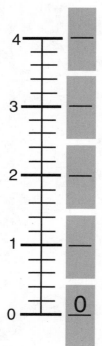

Lesson 48

Part 1

7	1__	21
2__	3__	4__
4__	5__	6__
70		

Part 2

4	8	12	16	20
24	28	32	36	40

a. 23 = 4 x _____ + _____

b. 15 = 4 x _____ + _____

c. 6 = 4 x _____ + _____

d. 10 = 4 x _____ + _____

e. 21 = 4 x _____ + _____

f. 39 = 4 x _____ + _____

38

Part 3

a. $3\overline{)12}$ b. $4\overline{)12}$ c. $4\overline{)20}$ d. $5\overline{)20}$ e. $4\overline{)16}$ f. $2\overline{)16}$

g. $4\overline{)8}$ h. $2\overline{)8}$ i. $9\overline{)54}$ j. $4\overline{)4}$ k. $4\overline{)36}$ l. $5\overline{)15}$

Part 4

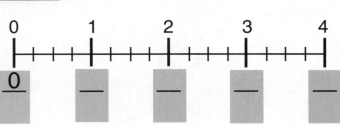

Part 5

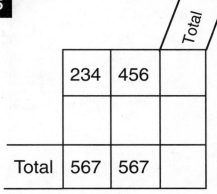

	234	456	Total
Total	567	567	

Lesson 49

Part 1

a. $3\overline{)615}$ b. $2\overline{)1016}$

Part 2

7	1__	2__
2__	___	___
___	5__	___
___		

Part 3

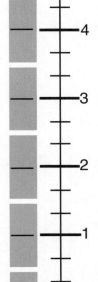

a. $\dfrac{14}{3}$ _____

b. $\dfrac{7}{3}$ _____

c. $\dfrac{11}{3}$ _____

	9
1	8
2	7
3	6
4	5
5	4
6	3
7	2
8	1
9	0

a. $30 = 9 \times \underline{\hspace{1cm}} + \underline{\hspace{1cm}}$

b. $48 = 9 \times \underline{\hspace{1cm}} + \underline{\hspace{1cm}}$

c. $60 = 9 \times \underline{\hspace{1cm}} + \underline{\hspace{1cm}}$

d. $22 = 9 \times \underline{\hspace{1cm}} + \underline{\hspace{1cm}}$

e. $75 = 9 \times \underline{\hspace{1cm}} + \underline{\hspace{1cm}}$

f. $13 = 9 \times \underline{\hspace{1cm}} + \underline{\hspace{1cm}}$

Test 5

Part 1

a. $4\overline{)28}$ f. $4\overline{)32}$

b. $4\overline{)16}$ g. $4\overline{)4}$

c. $4\overline{)24}$ h. $4\overline{)12}$

d. $4\overline{)0}$ i. $4\overline{)20}$

e. $4\overline{)36}$

Part 2

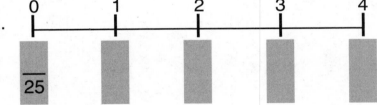

a. 4 7
   x 4 3
  +

b. 1 3
   x 8 2
  +

c. 3 4 5
   x   1 9
  +

Part 3

a. $3 + \dfrac{1}{5}$ b. $5 - \dfrac{5}{4}$ c. $\dfrac{27}{2} - 10$

Part 4

a.

0   1   2   3   4

$\overline{25}$

b. 4 — 3 — 2 — 1 — 0 —

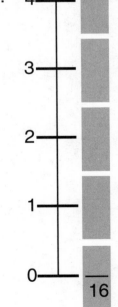

$\overline{16}$

Part 5

a. $4\overline{)328}$ b. $2\overline{)1206}$ c. $4\overline{)8400}$

Lesson 51

Part 1

__	1__	2__
2__	___	___
___	___	___
___		

Part 2

a. $3\overline{)1\ 2\ 6\ 9}$

b. $2\overline{)6\ 1\ 4}$

c. $5\overline{)5\ 3\ 5\ 0}$

d. $2\overline{)8\ 2\ 1\ 6}$

Independent Work

Part 3 Write the fractions for the whole numbers.

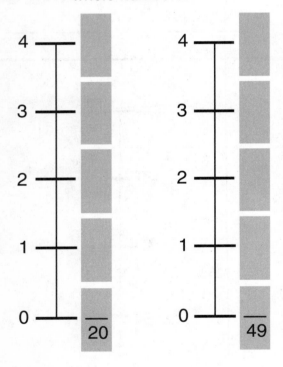

Part 4 Complete the equation for each problem.

4	8	12	16	20
24	28	32	36	40

a. $17 = 4 \times \underline{\ \ \ } + \underline{\ \ \ }$

b. $11 = 4 \times \underline{\ \ \ } + \underline{\ \ \ }$

c. $30 = 4 \times \underline{\ \ \ } + \underline{\ \ \ }$

d. $32 = 4 \times \underline{\ \ \ } + \underline{\ \ \ }$

Lesson 52

Part 1

a. $4\overline{)8\ 4\ 1\ 2}$

b. $3\overline{)6\ 2\ 7\ 9}$

c. $9\overline{)3\ 6\ 4\ 5\ 0}$

d. $5\overline{)5\ 1\ 5\ 5}$

Part 2

a. 14 = 4 x ___ + ___
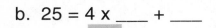

b. 25 = 4 x ___ + ___

c. 9 = 4 x ___ + ___

d. 11 = 4 x ___ + ___

e. 34 = 4 x ___ + ___

Part 3

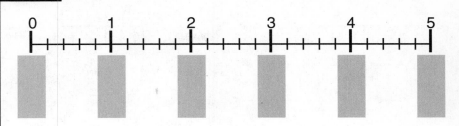

a. $\frac{12}{5}$

b. $\frac{9}{5}$

c. $\frac{16}{5}$

Independent Work

Part 4

a. $3\overline{)18}$ f. $4\overline{)4}$ k. $4\overline{)32}$

b. $4\overline{)16}$ g. $9\overline{)63}$ l. $4\overline{)12}$

c. $5\overline{)25}$ h. $3\overline{)24}$ m. $3\overline{)9}$

d. $9\overline{)81}$ i. $4\overline{)24}$ n. $3\overline{)0}$

e. $5\overline{)0}$ j. $3\overline{)27}$

Part 5   Complete the number map for counting by 7.

7	___	___
___	___	___
___	___	___
___		

Lesson 53

Part 1

a. 23 = 5 x ___ + ___

b. 21 = 5 x ___ + ___

c. 37 = 5 x ___ + ___

d. 34 = 5 x ___ + ___

e. 19 = 5 x ___ + ___

a. $3\overline{)69}$ b. $2\overline{)41216}$ c. $4\overline{)1208}$

Part 3

a. $5 \times \dfrac{1}{3}$ b. $\dfrac{4}{7} \times 3$ c. $\dfrac{3}{4} \times \dfrac{5}{6}$ d. $\dfrac{3}{3} \times 9$ e. $\dfrac{1}{5} \times \dfrac{8}{8}$

Lesson 54

Part 1

The table is supposed to show the number of boys and girls at Washington School and Roosevelt School.

	Boys	Girls	Total children
Washington School			146
Roosevelt School	36		
Total for both schools			

Fact 1: There were 82 boys in Washington School.

Fact 2: The total number of children in both schools was 237.

Fact 3: 55 girls went to Roosevelt School.

Part 2

a. $3\overline{)2412}$ b. $5\overline{)3515}$ c. $5\overline{)5045}$ d. $3\overline{)9186}$

Part 3 Complete the equations.

a. $15 = 4 \times \underline{} + \underline{}$

b. $18 = 4 \times \underline{} + \underline{}$

c. $6 = 4 \times \underline{} + \underline{}$

d. $37 = 4 \times \underline{} + \underline{}$

e. $23 = 4 \times \underline{} + \underline{}$

Part 4

a. $1\overline{)9}$ b. $3\overline{)9}$ c. $9\overline{)9}$ d. $9\overline{)36}$ e. $9\overline{)0}$ f. $3\overline{)15}$

g. $5\overline{)40}$ h. $5\overline{)30}$ i. $5\overline{)20}$ j. $9\overline{)27}$ k. $3\overline{)27}$

Lesson 55

Part 1

a. $4\overline{)2400}$ b. $2\overline{)6122}$ c. $9\overline{)36180}$

Part 2

a. $\dfrac{8}{2} =$ b. $\dfrac{}{2} = 8$

c. $\dfrac{}{3} = 6$ d. $\dfrac{20}{5} =$

Lesson 56

Part 1

a. $3\overline{)3906}$ b. $4\overline{)42812}$ c. $9\overline{)1809}$

a. $3 \times \frac{5}{5} = \boxed{}$

d. $\frac{5}{4} \times \frac{10}{10} = \boxed{}$

f. $9 \times \frac{2}{2} = \boxed{}$

b. $8 \times \frac{2}{3} = \boxed{}$

e. $4 \times \frac{6}{5} = \boxed{}$

g. $\frac{1}{4} \times \frac{1}{2} = \boxed{}$

c. $\frac{3}{5} \times \frac{4}{4} = \boxed{}$

Part 3

a. $14 = 3 \times \underline{} + \underline{}$

b. $14 = 5 \times \underline{} + \underline{}$

c. $14 = 9 \times \underline{} + \underline{}$

d. $20 = 9 \times \underline{} + \underline{}$

e. $25 = 4 \times \underline{} + \underline{}$

f. $25 = 3 \times \underline{} + \underline{}$

Lesson 57

Part 1

a. $\frac{20}{3} = 6 +$

b. $\frac{31}{4} = 7 +$

c. $\frac{15}{2} = 7 +$

d. $\frac{12}{8} = 1 +$

Part 2

a. $3 \times \frac{5}{4} = \boxed{}$

d. $\frac{7}{5} \times \frac{9}{9} = \boxed{}$

f. $\frac{4}{9} \times \frac{1}{1} = \boxed{}$

b. $3 \times \frac{5}{5} = \boxed{}$

e. $\frac{2}{10} \times \frac{8}{2} = \boxed{}$

g. $\frac{2}{31} \times \frac{0}{1} = \boxed{}$

c. $\frac{7}{5} \times \frac{1}{7} = \boxed{}$

Part 3

a. $9 \overline{\smash{)}2\,7\,9}$ 3 81

b. $4 \overline{\smash{)}8\,4}$ 32 1

c. $3 \overline{\smash{)}3\,6\,0}$ 1 18 0

d. $2 \overline{\smash{)}1\,6\,2}$ 8 4

46

Part 4

a. 17 = 5 x ___ + ___

b. 17 = 3 x ___ + ___

c. 17 = 4 x ___ + ___

d. 17 = 9 x ___ + ___

e. 17 = 2 x ___ + ___

Lesson 58

Part 1

1	2	3
4	5	6
7	8	9
10		

a. 7⟌2 1   d. 7⟌2 8   g. 7⟌7

b. 7⟌3 5   e. 7⟌4 2   h. 7⟌4 9

c. 7⟌5 6   f. 7⟌6 3   i. 7⟌0

Part 2

a. 26 = 7 x ___ + ___

b. 47 = 9 x ___ + ___

c. 38 = 9 x ___ + ___

d. 38 = 7 x ___ + ___

e. 85 = 9 x ___ + ___

Part 3

a. 2⟌1 2 8 (6 16)

b. 4⟌8 4 8 (2 1 32)

c. 4⟌8 2 0 (2 8 5)

d. 5⟌5 0 5 (1 0 25)

e. 3⟌6 3 (18 1)

47

Lesson 59

a. $\dfrac{7}{4} = 1 +$ b. $\dfrac{26}{7} = 3 +$ c. $\dfrac{19}{4} = 4 +$

d. $\dfrac{19}{5} = 3 +$ e. $\dfrac{19}{3} = 6 +$

Part 2

a. $\dfrac{2}{5} \times \boxed{} = \dfrac{10}{15}$ b. $\dfrac{4}{9} \times \boxed{} = \dfrac{12}{27}$ c. $\dfrac{5}{3} \times \boxed{} = \dfrac{15}{21}$

d. $6 \times \boxed{} = \dfrac{30}{5}$ e. $\dfrac{1}{4} \times \boxed{} = \dfrac{4}{36}$

Part 3

1	2	3
4	5	6
7	8	9
10		

a. $7\overline{)28}$ b. $7\overline{)0}$ c. $7\overline{)35}$ d. $7\overline{)56}$

e. $7\overline{)7}$ f. $7\overline{)42}$ g. $7\overline{)63}$ h. $7\overline{)21}$

Test 6

Part 1

a. 6 x 7 = ____

b. 7 x 9 = ____

c. 6 x 4 = ____

d. 0 x 7 = ____

e. 7 x 3 = ____

f. 3 x 6 = ____

g. 8 x 7 = ____

h. 7 x 4 = ____

i. 7 x 7 = ____

j. 7 x 1 = ____

k. 4 x 8 = ____

l. 2 x 7 = ____

Part 2

a. $7\overline{)63}$

b. $7\overline{)28}$

c. $7\overline{)49}$

d. $7\overline{)35}$

e. $7\overline{)42}$

f. $7\overline{)0}$

g. $7\overline{)21}$

h. $7\overline{)56}$

i. $7\overline{)7}$

Part 3

a. $\frac{21}{3}$

b. $\frac{24}{4}$

c. $\frac{20}{5}$

d. $\frac{72}{9}$

Part 4

a. $3 \times \frac{5}{5} = \frac{}{}$

b. $\frac{7}{2} \times \frac{3}{6} = \frac{}{}$

c. $\frac{5}{9} \times \frac{4}{4} = \frac{}{}$

Part 5

a. 17 = 9 x ____ + ____

b. 35 = 4 x ____ + ____

c. 50 = 9 x ____ + ____

Part 6

a. $\frac{}{4} = 8$

b. $\frac{6}{2} =$

c. $9 = \frac{}{3}$

d. $\frac{20}{5} =$

Part 7

a. $2\overline{)64}$

b. $4\overline{)1224}$

c. $3\overline{)6015}$

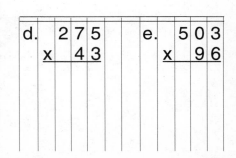

49

This table is supposed to show the number of boys and girls in the classrooms and on the playground.

	Boys	Girls	Total children
Classrooms			
Playground			
Total for both places			

Fact 1: There were 147 children in the classrooms.

Fact 2: There were 111 boys on the playground.

Fact 3: There were 183 children on the playground.

Fact 4: There were 64 girls in the classrooms.

Questions

a. How many boys were in the classrooms? _____

b. What's the total number of girls? _____

c. Were there more boys or more girls on the playground? _____

d. Were there more children in the classrooms or on the playground?

_____

Lesson 61

Part 1

a. $3 \times \dfrac{4}{3} =$

b. $3 - \dfrac{4}{3} =$

c. $6 + \dfrac{3}{7} =$

d. $8 \times \dfrac{5}{9} =$

e. $\dfrac{4}{5} \times 9 =$

f. $\dfrac{4}{5} + 9 =$

Part 2

a.

	Motorcycles	Bikes	Total for both vehicles
Hill Trail		26	121
Glacier Trail	19 ✔	✔	
Total for both trails			

Fact: On Glacier Trail, there were 28 more bikes than motorcycles.

b.

	Young trees	Old trees	Total trees
Road Park	231	✔	
Mountain Park		75 ✔	138
Total for both parks			

Fact: There were 34 fewer old trees in Road Park than in Mountain Park.

Part 3

a. $\dfrac{18}{3}$

b. $\dfrac{27}{3}$

c. $\dfrac{6}{3}$

d. $\dfrac{12}{3}$

Part 4

3	6	9
12	15	18
21	24	27
30		

a. $\dfrac{29}{3} = \underline{\quad} +$

b. $\dfrac{22}{3} = \underline{\quad} +$

c. $\dfrac{26}{3} = \underline{\quad} +$

d. $\dfrac{16}{3} = \underline{\quad} +$

Part 5

a. $7\overline{)49}$ b. $7\overline{)63}$ c. $7\overline{)42}$ d. $7\overline{)21}$

e. $7\overline{)56}$ f. $7\overline{)0}$ g. $7\overline{)28}$ h. $7\overline{)14}$

Lesson 62

Part 1

| This table is supposed to show the number of third graders and fourth graders in two schools. | This table is supposed to show the number of bikes and motorcycles on two trails. |

a.

	Third grade	Fourth grade	Total for both grades
Mason School	251✔	✔	
Evans School			
Total for both schools	553		934

b.

	Bikes	Motorcycles	Total for both vehicles
Glacier Trail		✔	180
Mountain Trail		268✔	402
Total for both trails			

Fact: In Mason School, there were 84 more third graders than fourth graders.

Fact: There were 187 fewer motorcycles on Glacier Trail than there were on Mountain Trail.

Part 2

5	10
15	20
25	30
35	40
45	50

a. $\dfrac{34}{5} = \underline{\quad} + \blacksquare$ b. $\dfrac{23}{5} = \underline{\quad} + \blacksquare$

c. $\dfrac{47}{5} = \underline{\quad} + \blacksquare$ d. $\dfrac{19}{5} = \underline{\quad} + \blacksquare$

a. $\dfrac{3}{4}$ x $\dfrac{5}{}$ = $\dfrac{}{28}$

b. $\dfrac{6}{2}$ x $\dfrac{}{7}$ = $\dfrac{24}{}$

c. $\dfrac{4}{5}$ x $\dfrac{9}{}$ = $\dfrac{}{45}$

d. $\dfrac{3}{7}$ x $\dfrac{}{7}$ = $\dfrac{6}{}$

e. $\dfrac{5}{4}$ x $\dfrac{4}{}$ = $\dfrac{}{20}$

a. $\dfrac{5}{3} + 8 =$

b. $\dfrac{7}{2} \times 4 =$

c. $3 - \dfrac{3}{4} =$

d. $\dfrac{2}{7} + 1 =$

e. $5 \times \dfrac{9}{7} =$

f. $5 - \dfrac{9}{7} =$

Lesson 63

These tables are supposed to show the number of blue cars and red cars on X Street and Y Street.

a.

10:00 AM	X Street	Y Street	Total for both streets
Blue cars	42✔		109
Red cars	✔	18	
Total for both cars			

b.

5:00 PM	X Street	Y Street	Total for both streets
Blue cars	✔	82✔	
Red cars			
Total for both cars	164	181	

Fact: On X Street, there are 12 more blue cars than red cars.

Fact: The number of blue cars on Y Street is 19 less than the number of blue cars on X Street.

53

Part 3

a. $\dfrac{13}{3}$ = —— +

b. $\dfrac{17}{3}$ = —— +

c. $\dfrac{17}{5}$ = —— +

d. $\dfrac{17}{4}$ = —— +

e. $\dfrac{28}{5}$ = —— +

6	
18	
30	
42	
54	

Part 4

a. $\dfrac{4}{6} \times \dfrac{3}{} = \dfrac{}{6}$

b. $\dfrac{7}{2} \times \dfrac{}{2} = \dfrac{14}{}$

c. $\dfrac{3}{1} \times \dfrac{}{8} = \dfrac{6}{}$

d. $\dfrac{5}{4} \times \dfrac{9}{} = \dfrac{}{36}$

Part 5

a. $6 \times \dfrac{7}{3} =$

b. $6 - \dfrac{7}{3} =$

c. $\dfrac{7}{3} + 8 =$

d. $\dfrac{5}{8} + 3 =$

e. $5 \times \dfrac{1}{9} =$

f. $5 - \dfrac{1}{9} =$

Lesson 64

Part 1

6	
18	
30	
42	
54	

Part 2

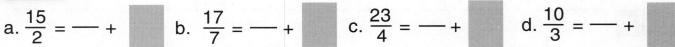

	□̄	▨ = —		□̄	▨ = —
a.	9)‾5‾4‾	$\frac{54}{9}$ = —	e.	3)‾2‾4‾	— = —
b.	5)‾3‾0‾	— = —	f.	9)‾1‾8‾	— = —
c.	7)‾2‾1‾	— = —	g.	5)‾1‾5‾	— = —
d.	4)‾8‾	— = —	h.	7)‾4‾2‾	— = —

Part 3

a. $\frac{15}{2}$ = — +   b. $\frac{17}{7}$ = — +   c. $\frac{23}{4}$ = — +   d. $\frac{10}{3}$ = — +

Part 4

a. $\frac{1}{5} \times \frac{6}{} = \frac{}{30}$

b. $\frac{5}{9} \times \frac{7}{} = \frac{}{45}$

c. $\frac{2}{7} \times \frac{}{8} = \frac{16}{}$

d. $\frac{10}{3} \times \frac{}{8} = \frac{60}{}$

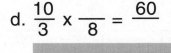

Lesson 65

a.	$7\overline{)28}$	$\dfrac{\ }{\ } = \dfrac{\ }{\ }$	d.	$9\overline{)81}$	$\dfrac{\ }{\ } = \dfrac{\ }{\ }$
b.		$\dfrac{54}{9} = \dfrac{\ }{\ }$	e.	$4\overline{)24}$	$\dfrac{\ }{\ } = \dfrac{\ }{\ }$
c.		$\dfrac{28}{4} = \dfrac{\ }{\ }$			

Part 2

a. 6 x 8 = ___   b. 6 x 2 = ___   c. 6 x 6 = ___   d. 6 x 4 = ___   e. 6 x 10 = ___

Part 3

This table is supposed to show the number of cars and trucks on two streets.

a.

	Cars	Trucks	Total for both vehicles
M Street	28		
Z Street		40	
Total for both streets		99	

Fact: On Z Street, there are 23 more cars than trucks.

This table is supposed to show the number of tulips and roses on two streets.

b.

	Tulips	Roses	Total for both flowers
B Street	21		
C Street		120	324
Total for both streets	225		

Fact: The number of roses on C Street is 31 less than the number on B Street.

Lesson 66

Part 1

a. $\dfrac{3}{5} \longrightarrow \dfrac{9}{5}$ b. $\dfrac{2}{12} \quad \dfrac{5}{12} \longrightarrow$ c. $\dfrac{9}{3} \longrightarrow \dfrac{14}{3}$

d. $\dfrac{6}{30} \quad \dfrac{10}{30} \longrightarrow$ e. $\dfrac{14}{1} \longrightarrow \dfrac{19}{1}$

Part 2

The table is supposed to show the number of tacos and hot dogs sold by two restaurants—Joe's Stand and Rose's Cafe.

	Tacos	Hot dogs	Total for both foods
Joe's Stand			
Rose's Cafe			
Total for both restaurants			

Fact 1: The total number of tacos and hot dogs sold by both places is 587.

Fact 2: Joe's Stand sold 148 hot dogs.

Fact 3: Together, Joe's Stand and Rose's Cafe sold 281 hot dogs.

Fact 4: Joe's Stand sold 56 fewer tacos than hot dogs.

Part 3

In each problem, the fraction you start with and the fraction you end up with are equal.

a. $\dfrac{3}{5} \times \dfrac{}{} = \dfrac{}{20}$

b. $\dfrac{7}{2} \times \dfrac{}{} = \dfrac{}{18}$

c. $\dfrac{3}{4} \times \dfrac{}{} = \dfrac{21}{}$

d. $\dfrac{6}{5} \times \dfrac{}{} = \dfrac{60}{}$

Part 4

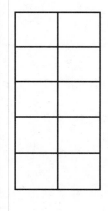

Part 5

$\square \times \underline{} = \square$	$\lceil$
a.	$4\overline{)28}$
b.	$3\overline{)24}$
c. $2 \times \underline{} = 16$	$\lceil$
d.	$4\overline{)8}$

Lesson 67

Part 1

a. ☐ $\xrightarrow{\frac{4}{7}}$ 1

b. $\frac{4}{9}$ $\xrightarrow{\quad 1 \quad}$ ☐

c. $\xrightarrow{\quad 1 \quad}$ ☐ $\frac{16}{10}$

d. $\frac{6}{7}$ $\xrightarrow{\quad ☐ \quad}$ 1

Part 2

a. 6 x 7 = _____

b. 6 x 2 = _____

c. 6 x 8 = _____

d. 6 x 4 = _____

e. 6 x 9 = _____

f. 6 x 3 = _____

g. 6 x 6 = _____

h. 6 x 5 = _____

Part 3

a. $\frac{3}{4}$ x ☐ = $\frac{☐}{20}$

b. $\frac{7}{9}$ x ☐ = $\frac{☐}{18}$

c. $\frac{7}{4}$ x ☐ = $\frac{21}{☐}$

d. $\frac{4}{5}$ x ☐ = $\frac{☐}{35}$

Part 4

☐ x ___ = ☐	$\overline{}$
a. 5 x _____ = 40	$\overline{}$
b.	7$\overline{)63}$
c.	9$\overline{)36}$
d.	7$\overline{)49}$
e. 7 x _____ = 56	$\overline{}$

Lesson 68

Part 1

Sample:

    39 = 4 x _____ + R _____

    ☐

a. 26 = 4 x _____ + R _____

    ☐

b. 50 = 9 x _____ + R _____

    ☐

c. 28 = 3 x _____ + R _____

    ☐

d. 15 = 2 x _____ + R _____

    ☐

e. 30 = 4 x _____ + R _____

    ☐

Part 2

a. 4$\overline{)344}$

b. 4$\overline{)924}$

c. 5$\overline{)805}$

a. $\dfrac{3}{2}$ x ___ = $\dfrac{21}{}$ b. $\dfrac{3}{4}$ x ___ = $\dfrac{}{24}$

c. $\dfrac{9}{7}$ x ___ = $\dfrac{45}{}$ d. $\dfrac{5}{9}$ x ___ = $\dfrac{}{54}$

Part 4

a. ___ $\xrightarrow{\ 1\ }$ $\dfrac{24}{20}$ b. $\dfrac{2}{11}$ $\xrightarrow{\ \ \ }$ 1

c. $\xrightarrow{\ 1\ }$ $\dfrac{41}{3}$ ___   d. ___ $\xrightarrow{\ \ \ }$ $\dfrac{5}{19}$ 1

Lesson 69

Part 1

a. $25 = 4 \times$ ___ $+ R$ ___

b. $38 = 5 \times$ ___ $+ R$ ___

c. $56 = 9 \times$ ___ $+ R$ ___

d. $20 = 7 \times$ ___ $+ R$ ___

e. $88 = 9 \times$ ___ $+ R$ ___

Part 2

a. $\dfrac{1}{2}$ $\xrightarrow{\ \ \ }$ 4

b. $\dfrac{2}{5}$ $\xrightarrow{\ 3\ }$ ___

c. ___ $\xrightarrow{\ \ \ }$ $\dfrac{2}{14}$ 1

d. $\xrightarrow{\ 1\ }$ $\dfrac{9}{31}$ ___

e. $\dfrac{12}{3}$ $\xrightarrow{\ \ \ }$ 6

Part 3

a. $\dfrac{2}{5}$ x ___ = $\dfrac{}{40}$

b. $\dfrac{10}{3}$ x ___ = $\dfrac{40}{}$

c. $\dfrac{4}{6}$ x ___ = $\dfrac{12}{}$

d. $\dfrac{1}{4}$ x ___ = $\dfrac{}{4}$

Part 4

a. $3\overline{)375}$ b. $3\overline{)138}$ c. $3\overline{)657}$

Test 7

Part 1

a. 2 x 2 = ___   e. 8 x 8 = ___   i. 6 x 4 = ___   m. 9 x 6 = ___

b. 7 x 7 = ___   f. 5 x 5 = ___   j. 5 x 6 = ___   n. 2 x 6 = ___

c. 4 x 4 = ___   g. 0 x 0 = ___   k. 1 x 6 = ___   o. 6 x 3 = ___

d. 6 x 6 = ___   h. 9 x 7 = ___   l. 6 x 7 = ___   p. 6 x 8 = ___

Part 2

a. $\dfrac{23}{7} =$ b. $\dfrac{38}{5} =$ c. $\dfrac{61}{9} =$

Part 3

The table is supposed to show the number of boys and girls at Washington School and Roosevelt School.

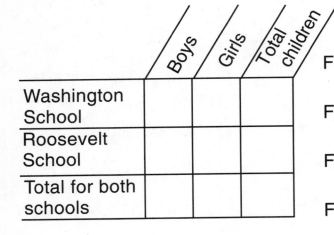

	Boys	Girls	Total children
Washington School			
Roosevelt School			
Total for both schools			

Fact 1: 146 children went to Washington School.

Fact 2: 26 boys went to Roosevelt School.

Fact 3: 82 girls went to Washington School.

Fact 4: At Roosevelt School, there were 19 fewer boys than girls.

Part 4

a. $\dfrac{7}{2}$ x $\dfrac{\blacksquare}{\blacksquare} = \dfrac{63}{\blacksquare}$ b. $\dfrac{4}{9}$ x $\dfrac{\blacksquare}{\blacksquare} = \dfrac{\blacksquare}{54}$

Lesson 70

Part 1

a. $4\overline{)216}$　　b. $4\overline{)860}$　　c. $4\overline{)476}$　　d. $4\overline{)268}$

Lesson 71

Part 1

a. $3 \times \blacksquare = 1$

　more than 1

　less than 1

b. $3 \times \blacksquare = 5$

　more than 1

　less than 1

c. $5 \times \blacksquare = 4$

　more than 1

　less than 1

d. $2 \times \blacksquare = 3$

　more than 1

　less than 1

e. $11 \times \blacksquare = 14$

　more than 1

　less than 1

Part 2

a. There are 4 boys for every 7 girls. There are 21 girls. How many boys are there? _____

$\dfrac{\text{boys}}{\text{girls}}\quad \dfrac{4}{7} \times \dfrac{}{} = \dfrac{}{}$

b. There are 3 perch for every 7 bass. There are 28 bass. How many perch are there? _____

$\dfrac{\text{perch}}{\text{bass}}\quad \dfrac{}{} \times \dfrac{}{} = \dfrac{}{}$

c. There are 6 dogs for every 5 cats. There are 18 dogs. How many cats are there? _____

$\dfrac{\text{dogs}}{\text{cats}}\quad \dfrac{}{} \times \dfrac{}{} = \dfrac{}{}$

d. There are 3 frogs for every 4 fish. There are 21 frogs. How many fish are there? _____

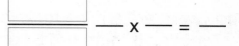

Part 3

a. $3\overline{)624}$　　b. $5\overline{)590}$　　c. $5\overline{)235}$　　d. $3\overline{)126}$　　e. $2\overline{)674}$

Lesson 72

Part 1

a. $3 \times \blacksquare = 2$

more than 1

less than 1

b. $5 \times \blacksquare = 1$

more than 1

less than 1

c. $54 \times \blacksquare = 64$

more than 1

less than 1

d. $45 \times \blacksquare = 54$

more than 1

less than 1

e. $\dfrac{2}{1} \times \blacksquare = \dfrac{1}{1}$

more than 1

less than 1

f. $\dfrac{12}{1} \times \blacksquare = \dfrac{16}{1}$

more than 1

less than 1

Part 2

a. $\dfrac{4}{5}$ $\dfrac{5}{4}$

b. $\dfrac{7}{7}$ $\dfrac{3}{2}$

c. $\dfrac{3}{3}$ $\dfrac{7}{8}$

d. $\dfrac{5}{3}$ $\dfrac{6}{7}$

e. $\dfrac{3}{5}$ $\dfrac{2}{1}$

Part 3

a. There are 10 fleas for every 7 dogs. If there are 21 dogs, how many fleas are there? _____

$\dfrac{}{} \times \dfrac{}{} = \dfrac{}{}$

b. There are 3 trees for every 8 nuts. If there are 12 trees, how many nuts are there? _____

$\dfrac{}{} \times \dfrac{}{} = \dfrac{}{}$

c. There are 7 cars for each truck. If there are 28 cars, how many trucks are there? _____

$\dfrac{}{} \times \dfrac{}{} = \dfrac{}{}$

d. There are 5 mice for every 9 seeds. If there are 54 seeds, how many mice are there? _____

$\dfrac{}{} \times \dfrac{}{} = \dfrac{}{}$

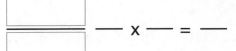

a. $(x = 4, y = 3)$

b. $(x = 6, y = 2)$

c. $(x = 1, y = 4)$

d. $(x = 7, y = 5)$

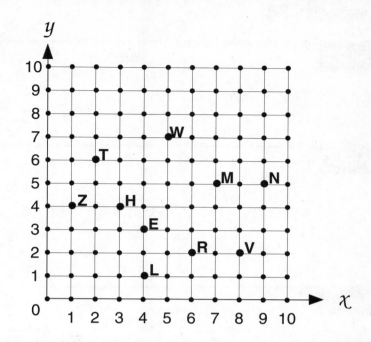

Lesson 73

Part 1

a. $2\overline{)7016}$ b. $7\overline{)9135}$ c. $7\overline{)1421}$ d. $4\overline{)8760}$

Part 2

a. $31 \times \blacksquare = 30$

more than 1

less than 1

b. $7 \times \blacksquare = 8$

more than 1

less than 1

c. $6 \times \blacksquare = \dfrac{7}{7}$

more than 1

less than 1

d. $\dfrac{4}{9} \times \blacksquare = \dfrac{8}{9}$

more than 1

less than 1

e. $\dfrac{10}{11} \times \blacksquare = \dfrac{9}{1}$

more than 1

less than 1

Lesson 74

Part 1

a. $\dfrac{7}{6}$ $\dfrac{11}{12}$ b. $\dfrac{10}{4}$ $\dfrac{13}{4}$ c. $\dfrac{7}{5}$ $\dfrac{8}{8}$ d. $\dfrac{4}{7}$ $\dfrac{3}{2}$ e. $\dfrac{12}{8}$ $\dfrac{17}{8}$

Part 2

a. $3\overline{)4\,8\,1\,2}$ b. $7\overline{)6\,3\,9\,8}$ c. $2\overline{)3\,6\,7\,2}$ d. $9\overline{)3\,6\,7\,2}$

Part 3

a. $\left(\dfrac{6}{8}\right) \times \blacksquare = \dfrac{2}{3}$

more than 1

less than 1

b. $\dfrac{4}{5} \times \blacksquare = \left(\dfrac{7}{8}\right)$

more than 1

less than 1

c. $\left(\dfrac{2}{8}\right) \times \blacksquare = \dfrac{4}{18}$

more than 1

less than 1

d. $\left(\dfrac{2}{1}\right) \times \blacksquare = \dfrac{16}{12}$

more than 1

less than 1

e. $\left(\dfrac{11}{5}\right) \times \blacksquare = \dfrac{8}{7}$

more than 1

less than 1

f. $\dfrac{12}{3} \times \blacksquare = \left(\dfrac{19}{1}\right)$

more than 1

less than 1

Lesson 75

Part 1

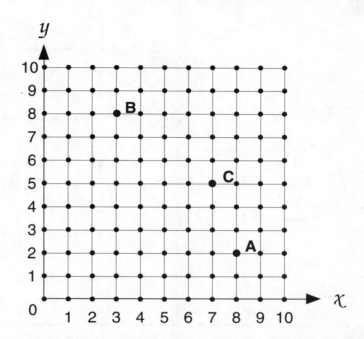

A   ($x=$ ___, $y=$ ___)

B   ($x=$ ___, $y=$ ___)

C   ($x=$ ___, $y=$ ___)

Part 2

a. $\dfrac{8}{6} \times \blacksquare = \dfrac{1}{3}$

more than 1

less than 1

b. $\dfrac{6}{5} \times \blacksquare = \dfrac{12}{13}$

more than 1

less than 1

c. $\dfrac{8}{10} \times \blacksquare = \dfrac{7}{7}$

more than 1

less than 1

d. $\dfrac{2}{1} \times \blacksquare = \dfrac{1}{12}$

more than 1

less than 1

e. $\dfrac{4}{5} \times \blacksquare = \dfrac{3}{2}$

more than 1

less than 1

Part 3

a. $4\overline{)144}$ b. $4\overline{)6812}$ c. $3\overline{)68112}$ d. $2\overline{)1058}$ e. $3\overline{)9315}$

Lesson 76

Part 1

A ($x=$ ___, $y=$ ___)

B ($x=$ ___, $y=$ ___)

C ($x=$ ___, $y=$ ___)

D ($x=$ ___, $y=$ ___)

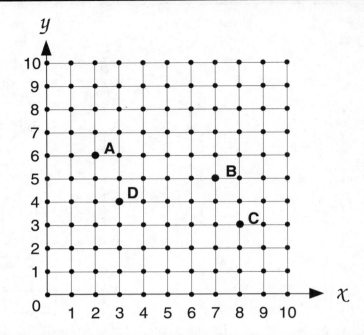

Part 2

a. $7\overline{)8428}$ b. $5\overline{)1030}$ c. $4\overline{)29292}$ d. $5\overline{)5075}$

Lesson 77

Part 1

x	Function	Answer
	$x+5$	■
4		
1		
6		
8		

Part 2

a. $\dfrac{2}{2}$ × ■ = $\dfrac{8}{6}$

more than 1

less than 1

b. $\dfrac{5}{7}$ × ■ = $\dfrac{6}{7}$

more than 1

less than 1

c. $\dfrac{12}{12}$ × ■ = $\dfrac{14}{18}$

more than 1

less than 1

d. $\dfrac{10}{13}$ × ■ = $\dfrac{6}{4}$

more than 1

less than 1

Part 3 Work each problem.

a. $4\overline{)2924}$ b. $3\overline{)5127}$ c. $2\overline{)1806}$ d. $9\overline{)9396}$

Lesson 78

Part 1

	Function	Answer
x	$x \times 3$	
a. 4		
b. 8		
c. $\frac{3}{16}$		
d. 10		
e. $\frac{1}{5}$		

Part 2

a. $\frac{37}{4} \times \blacksquare = \frac{60}{60}$

　more than 1

　less than 1

b. $\frac{2}{5} \times \blacksquare = \frac{4}{5}$

　more than 1

　less than 1

c. $\frac{15}{20} \times \blacksquare = \frac{6}{1}$

　more than 1

　less than 1

d. $\frac{5}{5} \times \blacksquare = \frac{14}{15}$

　more than 1

　less than 1

e. $\frac{1}{3} \times \blacksquare = \frac{3}{1}$

　more than 1

　less than 1

Part 3

	$\square \times \underline{} = \square$	$\overline{)}$	$\square = \square$
a.	$4 \times \underline{} = 36$	$\overline{)}$	$\blacksquare = \blacksquare$
b.		$7\overline{)56}$	
c.		$6\overline{)54}$	
d.		$\overline{)}$	$\frac{15}{3} = \blacksquare$

Part 4 | Write the answers.

6	12
18	24
30	36
42	48
54	60

a. $6\overline{)24}$

b. $6\overline{)54}$

c. $6\overline{)48}$

d. $6\overline{)30}$

e. $6\overline{)12}$

f. $6\overline{)36}$

Lesson 79

Part 1

	Function	Answer
x	$\dfrac{x}{3}$	
a. 12	$\dfrac{12}{3}$	
b. 63		
c. 6		
d. 3		
e. 24		

Part 2

a. $\dfrac{4}{5} \times \blacksquare = \dfrac{18}{2}$

more than 1

less than 1

b. $\dfrac{3}{4} \times \blacksquare = \dfrac{1}{4}$

more than 1

less than 1

c. $\dfrac{7}{3} \times \blacksquare = \dfrac{11}{11}$

more than 1

less than 1

d. $\dfrac{2}{3} \times \blacksquare = \dfrac{9}{1}$

more than 1

less than 1

e. $\dfrac{5}{8} \times \blacksquare = \dfrac{2}{2}$

more than 1

less than 1

Part 3 | Write the answers.

6	12
18	24
30	36
42	48
54	60

a. $6\overline{)48}$

b. $4\overline{)24}$

c. $7\overline{)42}$

d. $4\overline{)12}$

e. $6\overline{)54}$

f. $4\overline{)32}$

g. $7\overline{)28}$

h. $3\overline{)12}$

i. $6\overline{)24}$

j. $4\overline{)28}$

k. $7\overline{)49}$

l. $6\overline{)12}$

Test 8

a. 4 x 8 = ___   e. 5 x 0 = ___   i. 9 x 8 = ___   m. 6 x 8 = ___

b. 3 x 7 = ___   f. 8 x 1 = ___   j. 4 x 3 = ___   n. 1 x 7 = ___

c. 7 x 6 = ___   g. 6 x 4 = ___   k. 7 x 8 = ___   o. 9 x 4 = ___

d. 2 x 9 = ___   h. 3 x 8 = ___   l. 6 x 5 = ___   p. 6 x 3 = ___

Part 2

A $(x=$ ___ , $y=$ ___)

B $(x=$ ___ , $y=$ ___)

C $(x=$ ___ , $y=$ ___)

D $(x=$ ___ , $y=$ ___)

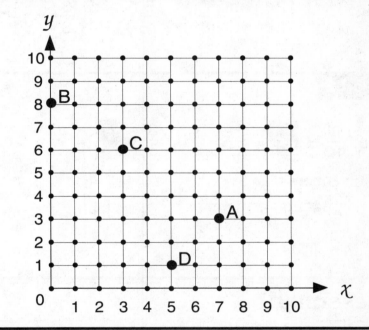

Part 3

	□ x ___ = □	⌐	□ = ⎯
a.	5 x _____ = 35	⌐	▓ ⎯ = ⎯
b.	□ x _____ = □	7⌐4 2	▓ ⎯ = ⎯
c.	□ x _____ = □	⌐	$\frac{28}{4}$ = ⎯
d.	□ x _____ = □	⌐	$\frac{155}{5}$ = ⎯

69

a. $3\overline{)5715}$ b. $4\overline{)1568}$ c. $2\overline{)7014}$

Lesson 80

Part 1

a. $\dfrac{3}{7}$ $\dfrac{12}{28}$ | b. $\dfrac{3}{8}$ $\dfrac{6}{16}$ | c. $\dfrac{3}{8}$ $\dfrac{12}{16}$ | d. $\dfrac{5}{1}$ $\dfrac{15}{4}$ | e. $\dfrac{5}{1}$ $\dfrac{30}{6}$

Part 2

a. $\dfrac{11}{12} \times$ ▮ $= \dfrac{12}{11}$

more than 1

less than 1

b. $\dfrac{3}{5} \times$ ▮ $= \dfrac{2}{2}$

more than 1

less than 1

c. $\dfrac{2}{1} \times$ ▮ $= \dfrac{20}{20}$

more than 1

less than 1

d. $\dfrac{13}{7} \times$ ▮ $= \dfrac{1}{13}$

more than 1

less than 1

Lesson 81

Part 1

a. $\dfrac{3}{4} \times$ ▮ $=$ ▮

more than 1

_____ than _____

b. $\dfrac{3}{4} \times$ ▮ $=$ ▮

less than 1

_____ than _____

c. $\dfrac{6}{6} \times$ ▮ $=$ ▮

less than 1

_____ than _____

d. $\dfrac{5}{7} \times$ ▮ $=$ ▮

more than 1

_____ than _____

	Function	Answer
x	$x - 3$	
a. 11		
b. 5		
c. 27		
d. 30		
e. 3		

Part 3

a. $\dfrac{3}{7}$ $\dfrac{12}{21}$

b. $\dfrac{3}{2}$ $\dfrac{12}{12}$

c. $\dfrac{3}{2}$ $\dfrac{12}{8}$

d. $\dfrac{7}{8}$ $\dfrac{14}{16}$

e. $\dfrac{6}{5}$ $\dfrac{42}{35}$

Independent Work

Part 4

a. $6\overline{)36}$ b. $6\overline{)54}$ c. $6\overline{)24}$ d. $6\overline{)18}$ e. $6\overline{)48}$

Lesson 82

Part 1

a. _____ + 1 = 20

b. _____ + 1 = 90

c. _____ + 1 = 300

d. _____ + 1 = 700

Part 2

a. $\begin{array}{r} 706 \\ -\ 29 \\ \hline \end{array}$

b. $\begin{array}{r} 302 \\ -\ 26 \\ \hline \end{array}$

c. $\begin{array}{r} 6001 \\ -\ 247 \\ \hline \end{array}$

Part 3

a. $\dfrac{7}{2}$ × ▮ = ▮

more than 1

_____ than ☐

b. 5 × ▮ = ▮

more than 1

_____ than ☐

c. $\dfrac{1}{5}$ × ▮ = ▮

less than 1

_____ than ☐

d. $\dfrac{7}{3}$ × ▮ = ▮

less than 1

_____ than ☐

Part 4

x	Function $\dfrac{x}{7}$	Answer
427		
63		
7		
0		
280		

Lesson 83

Part 1

a. 1 + _____ = 900

b. 1 + _____ = 30

c. 1 + _____ = 200

d. 1 + _____ = 800

Part 2

a.
$$\begin{array}{r} 304 \\ -25 \\ \hline \end{array}$$

b.
$$\begin{array}{r} 7006 \\ -309 \\ \hline \end{array}$$

c.
$$\begin{array}{r} 2008 \\ -517 \\ \hline \end{array}$$

Part 3

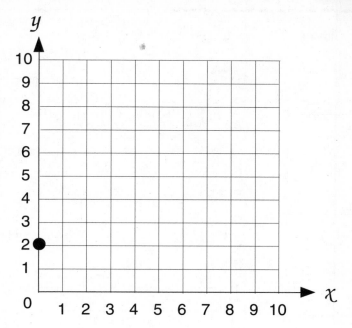

Part 4 Write the answers.

a. 6⟌42 g. 6⟌54

b. 6⟌36 h. 6⟌24

c. 6⟌48 i. 6⟌12

d. 7⟌42 j. 7⟌56

e. 7⟌63 k. 7⟌35

f. 7⟌49 l. 7⟌28

Lesson 84

Part 1

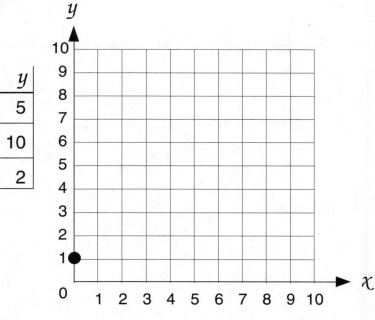

Part 2

a. 6⟌42 f. 7⟌42

b. 6⟌24 g. 7⟌49

c. 6⟌54 h. 7⟌28

d. 6⟌48 i. 7⟌56

e. 6⟌18 j. 7⟌63

Lesson 85

	x	Function $x-2$	Answer y
A	5		
B	3		
C	9		

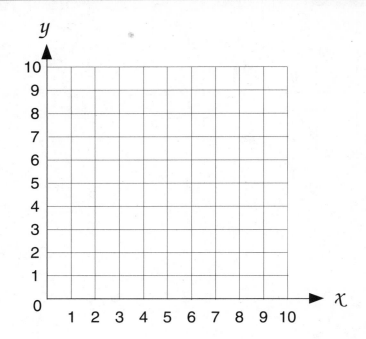

Independent Work

Part 2

a. $6\overline{)24}$ b. $6\overline{)36}$ c. $6\overline{)48}$ d. $6\overline{)30}$

e. $7\overline{)63}$ f. $7\overline{)42}$ g. $7\overline{)28}$ h. $7\overline{)49}$

Part 3

a. $17 = 2 \times$ ____ $+ R$ ____

b. $86 = 9 \times$ ____ $+ R$ ____

c. $59 = 7 \times$ ____ $+ R$ ____

d. $40 = 6 \times$ ____ $+ R$ ____

Lesson 86

Part 1

	x	Function x x 2	y
A	3		
B	5		
C	1		

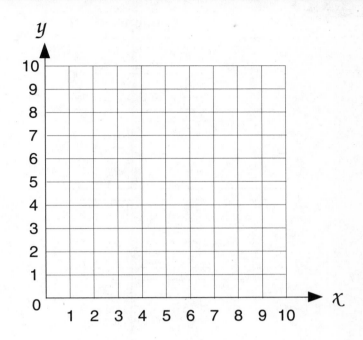

Lesson 87

Part 1

	x	Function $\frac{x}{2}$	y
A	10		
B	2		
C	6		
D	8		

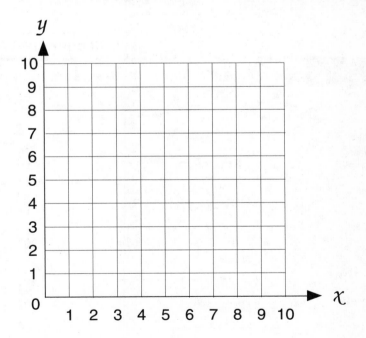

Lesson 88

	x	Function		y
A	5	5 × ▨		10
		5 + ▨		
B	2	▨ × ▨		8
		▨ + ▨		
C	6	▨ × ▨		12
		▨ + ▨		
D	5	▨ × ▨		15
		▨ + ▨		
E	1	▨ × ▨		1
		▨ + ▨		

Independent Work

Part 2   Complete the function table. Plot the points and draw the line.

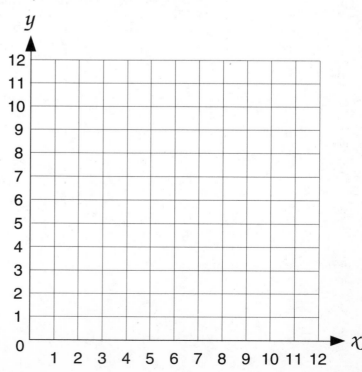

	x	Function $x \times 3$	y
A	0		
B	4		
C	1		

Lesson 89

Part 1

	x	Function	y
A	5	x ▓ x ▓	15
B	3	x ▓ x ▓	12
C	2	x ▓ x ▓	12

Part 2 Write the answers.

a. $6\overline{)48}$ b. $6\overline{)12}$

c. $6\overline{)24}$ d. $6\overline{)54}$

Part 3 Complete the table.

	$\square \times \underline{\quad} = \square$	$\overline{)}$	$\square = \dfrac{}{}$
a.	7 × _____ = 49		
b.			$\dfrac{35}{5}$
c.	3 × _____ = 207		

77

Test 9

Part 1

a. $6\overline{)4\,2}$ d. $6\overline{)6}$ g. $6\overline{)4\,8}$

b. $6\overline{)1\,8}$ e. $6\overline{)3\,6}$ h. $6\overline{)2\,4}$

c. $6\overline{)3\,0}$ f. $6\overline{)1\,2}$ i. $6\overline{)5\,4}$

Part 2

Circle more than 1, = 1 or less than 1 for each missing number.

a. $4 \times \blacksquare = \dfrac{15}{3}$

more than 1

= 1

less than 1

b. $\dfrac{3}{2} \times \blacksquare = \dfrac{15}{17}$

more than 1

= 1

less than 1

c. $\dfrac{2}{3} \times \blacksquare = \dfrac{8}{12}$

more than 1

= 1

less than 1

d. $\dfrac{9}{14} \times \blacksquare = \dfrac{3}{3}$

more than 1

= 1

less than 1

Part 3

a. $\begin{array}{r} 7006 \\ -2648 \\ \hline \end{array}$ b. $\begin{array}{r} 2008 \\ -1605 \\ \hline \end{array}$ c. $\begin{array}{r} 4003 \\ -\ 382 \\ \hline \end{array}$

Part 4

	x	Function $x-3$	y
A	3		
B	9		
C	5		

Lesson 91

Part 1

	Decimal Number	Mixed Number
	☐.☐	☐ + $\frac{☐}{100}$
a.	6.12	
b.	13.02	
c.	1.88	
d.	10.40	
e.	100.01	

Part 2

Sample Problem:

x	Function	y
2	$x \times 3$ $x + 4$	6

	x	Function	y
A	2		8
B	4		8
C	3		9
D	1		5

Part 3

a. $ 3.62
  x 12

b. $ 7.04
     x 9

c. $ 1.83
    x 90

Part 4

	thousands	hundreds	tens	ones
a.	7	6	8	6
b.	2	4	7	9
c.	3	7	4	8
d.	3	4	7	8
e.	8	1	9	0
f.	1	5	9	0

Part 5 Complete the table. Plot the points and draw the line.

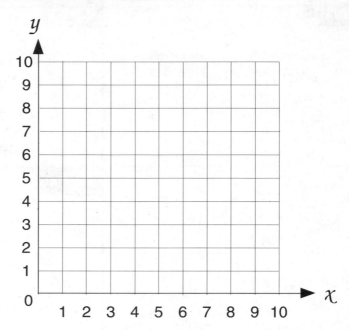

	x	Function $x + 2$	y
A	3		
B	0		
C	5		

Lesson 92

Part 1

	x	Function	y
A	8		4
B	6		2
C	12		3
D	6		18

Part 2

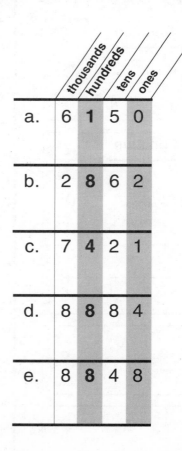

	thousands	hundreds	tens	ones
a.	6	**1**	5	0
b.	2	**8**	6	2
c.	7	**4**	2	1
d.	8	**8**	8	4
e.	8	**8**	4	8

Lesson 93

Part 1   Black balls are the winners.

a.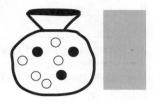

If I took ___ trials, I would expect ___ winner(s).

b.

If I took ___ trials, I would expect ___ winner(s).

c.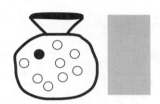

If I took ___ trials, I would expect ___ winner(s).

d.

If I took ___ trials, I would expect ___ winner(s).

Part 2

a.

x	Function	y
4	$x \times 2$ / $x + 4$	8
6		10
1		
2		
0		

b.

x	Function	y
3	$x - 2$ / $\dfrac{x}{3}$	1
9		3
5		
27		
12		

Part 3

a. 3 6 4 9   b. 3 6 7 9   c. 1 4 0 9   d. 2 8 4 3   e. 1 6 6 2

Part 4

	$\square . \square$	$\square + \dfrac{\square}{100}$
a.	4.15	
b.		$1 + \dfrac{6}{100}$
c.		$7 + \dfrac{4}{100}$
d.	1.03	

Part 5

Write the two simple functions for each item.

	x	Function	y
A	6		12
B	14		7
C	12		2
D	9		1

Lesson 94

a.

x	$x - 2$ $\frac{x}{2}$	y
4		2
6		4
11		
2		
5		

b.

x	$x + 6$ $x \times 3$	y
3		9
5		11
0		
4		
1		

Part 2 The winners for these sets are triangles.

a.

If I took ____ trials, I would expect ____ winner(s).

_____

b.

If I took ____ trials, I would expect ____ winner(s).

_____

c.

If I took ____ trials, I would expect ____ winner(s).

Part 3

a. 1 8 0 9

b. 5 7 6 2

c. 2 0 3 8

d. 5 1 1 5

e. 3 0 7 2

Part 4 Complete each table.

☐.☐	☐ + $\frac{☐}{100}$
3.60	
3.06	
	$11 + \frac{44}{100}$
	$6 + \frac{3}{100}$

☐.☐	$\frac{☐}{100}$
5.06	
3.12	
	$\frac{188}{100}$
	$\frac{506}{100}$

Lesson 95

Part 1

	x	Function	y
		x	
		x	
A	7		14
B	0		7
C	2		
D	5		
E	3		

Part 2

	☐ + $\frac{☐}{100}$	$\frac{☐}{100}$
a.	$5 + \frac{3}{100}$	
b.	$7 + \frac{94}{100}$	
c.	$13 + \frac{20}{100}$	
d.	$1 + \frac{8}{100}$	
e.	$100 + \frac{12}{100}$	

Part 3   Complete the function table. Plot the points and draw the line.

	Function	
	x	$\dfrac{x}{2}$	y
A	4		
B	10		
C	0		

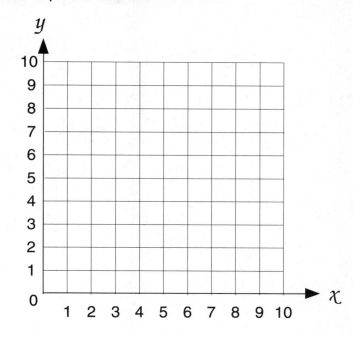

Lesson 96

Part 1

a. $\dfrac{3}{7}$ $\dfrac{12}{21}$

b. $\dfrac{1}{5}$ $\dfrac{6}{35}$

c. $\dfrac{2}{9}$ $\dfrac{6}{27}$

d. $\dfrac{7}{4}$ $\dfrac{42}{20}$

Part 2

	x	Function		y
		x		
		x		
A	1			4
B	3			12
C	5			
D	2			
E	0			

	Decimal Number ■.■	Mixed Number ■ + ■/100	Fraction ■/100
a.			$\dfrac{307}{100}$
b.			$\dfrac{1105}{100}$
c.		$1 + \dfrac{67}{100}$	
d.	10.50		
e.	71.09		

Independent Work

Part 4 The winners for these sets are **✗**'s.
Write the fraction for each bag and complete the statement.

a.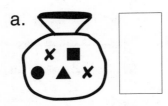

If I took ____ trials, I'd expect ____ winner(s).

b.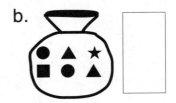

If I took ____ trials, I'd expect ____ winner(s).

c.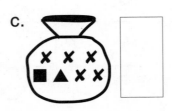

If I took ____ trials, I'd expect ____ winner(s).

Lesson 97

Part 1

Line 1

	x	Function	y
A			
B			
C			

Line 2

	x	Function	y
A			
B			
C			

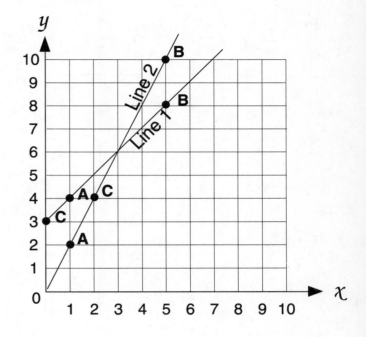

Part 2

	Decimal Number ■.■	Mixed Number ■ + ■/■	Fraction ■/■
a.			$\frac{1201}{100}$
b.	6.38		
c.		$1 + \frac{6}{100}$	

Part 3

a. $12 \div 3 =$ _____

b. $12 \div 6 =$ _____

c. $15 \div 3 =$ _____

d. $49 \div 7 =$ _____

e. $72 \div 9 =$ _____

f. $20 \div 5 =$ _____

g. $24 \div 6 =$ _____

h. $21 \div 7 =$ _____

Lesson 98

Line 1

x	Function	y
A		
B		
C		

Line 2

x	Function	y
A		
B		
C		

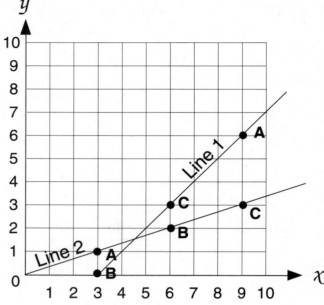

Part 2

Sample Problem:

$$\frac{6}{4} \times \frac{\quad}{\quad} = \frac{\quad}{100} = \quad .$$

a. $\frac{3}{4} \times \frac{\quad}{\quad} = \frac{\quad}{100} = \quad .$

b. $\frac{15}{5} \times \frac{\quad}{\quad} = \frac{\quad}{100} = \quad .$

Part 3

a. $27 \div 3 = \underline{\quad}$

b. $28 \div 4 = \underline{\quad}$

c. $30 \div 5 = \underline{\quad}$

d. $36 \div 6 = \underline{\quad}$

This table is supposed to show the inches of snow that fell in River City and Hill Town for two months.

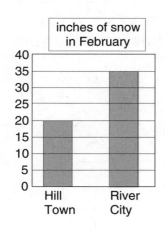

inches of snow in February

	February	March	Total
River City		24	
Hill Town			69
Total for both places			

Questions:

a. In Hill Town, did more snow fall during February or during March?

_____

b. During February, what were the total inches of snowfall?

_____

c. How many more inches of snow fell during March than February?

_____

d. How many more inches of snow fell in Hill Town than in River City?

_____

Lesson 99

Part 1

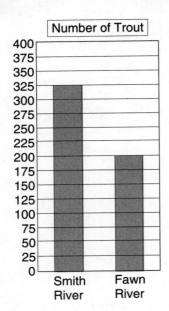

Number of Trout

This table is supposed to show the number of trout and bass in two rivers.

	Smith River	Fawn River	Total for both rivers
Trout			
Bass			
Total for both fish		496	997

Questions:

a. Which river had more trout? _____

b. Which river had fewer bass? _____

c. In the Smith River, were there more bass or trout? _____

Part 2

a. $\dfrac{1}{4}$ x —— = $\dfrac{}{100}$ = ___ .

b. $\dfrac{8}{10}$ x —— = $\dfrac{}{100}$ = ___ .

c. $\dfrac{7}{2}$ x —— = $\dfrac{}{100}$ = ___ .

d. $\dfrac{3}{5}$ x —— = $\dfrac{}{100}$ = ___ .

Test 10

Part 1

a. 24 ÷ 4 =

b. 36 ÷ 9 =

c. 42 ÷ 6 =

d. 21 ÷ 7 =

e. 8 ÷ 1 =

f. 18 ÷ 3 =

Part 2   The winners for these sets are ●'s.   **Part 3**

a.

If I took ___ trials, I would expect ___ winner(s).

b.

If I took ___ trials, I would expect ___ winner(s).

	Function	
x		y
A		
B		
C		

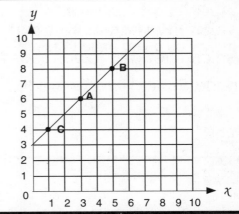

Lesson 100

Part 1

a. 1 2 4 ___ ___ ___

Rule

b. 12 10 8 ___ ___ ___

Rule

c. 3 6 9 ___ ___ ___

Rule

Part 2

Set a. $\dfrac{15}{16}$ $\dfrac{15}{5}$ $\dfrac{15}{14}$ $\dfrac{15}{1}$ $\dfrac{15}{15}$

Set b. $\dfrac{16}{8}$ $\dfrac{16}{48}$ $\dfrac{16}{2}$ $\dfrac{16}{100}$ $\dfrac{16}{14}$

Lesson 101

Part 1

a. $\dfrac{27}{72}$ $\dfrac{27}{3}$ $\dfrac{27}{1}$ $\dfrac{27}{27}$ $\dfrac{27}{30}$ $\dfrac{27}{26}$

b. $\dfrac{12}{4}$ $\dfrac{12}{3}$ $\dfrac{12}{24}$ $\dfrac{12}{6}$ $\dfrac{12}{16}$ $\dfrac{12}{36}$

Part 2

a.  For this set, the winners are black squares.
If you took 18 trials, about how many winners would you expect? _____

b. For this set, if you took 3 trials, you'd expect to get 1 winner.
About how many winners would you get if you took 450 trials? _____

c. For this set, if you took 7 trials you'd expect to get 5 winners.
To get 100 winners, about how many trials would you have to take? _____

d. For this set, the winners are white squares.
To get 100 winners, about how many trials would you have to take? _____

Part 3

Rule

a. 3, $3\frac{1}{2}$, 4, $4\frac{1}{2}$, ____, ____

Rule

b. 1, 3, 9, ____, ____

Lesson 102

Part 1

a. $2\frac{1}{2}$, 2, $1\frac{1}{2}$, 1, ____, ____

Rule

b. 1, 4, 16, ____, ____,

Rule

c. 4, $4\frac{1}{3}$, $4\frac{2}{3}$, ____, ____

Rule

Lesson 103

Part 1

a. $\frac{11}{3}$, $\frac{9}{3}$, $\frac{7}{3}$, ____, ____, ____

Rule

b. $\frac{1}{2}$, $2\frac{1}{2}$, $4\frac{1}{2}$, ____, ____

Rule

c. 11, 15, 19, ____, ____

Rule

Lesson 104

Part 1

a. 16,   8,   4, ____, ____

Rule

b. $6\frac{1}{3}$, $6\frac{2}{3}$,   7, ____, ____, ____

Rule

c. 3,   6,   12, ____, ____

Rule

Lesson 105

Part 1

a. $\frac{1}{2}$ $= \frac{}{100} =$.

b. $\frac{3}{50}$ $= \frac{}{100} =$.

c. $\frac{31}{10}$ $= \frac{}{100} =$.

d. $\frac{6}{5}$ $= \frac{}{100} =$.

e. $\frac{7}{4}$ $= \frac{}{100} =$.

f. $\frac{1}{5}$ $= \frac{}{100} =$.

Part 2

a. $\frac{1}{3}$, $\frac{3}{3}$, $\frac{9}{3}$, ____, ____

Rule

b. $\frac{1}{5}$, $\frac{2}{15}$, $\frac{4}{45}$, ____, ____

Rule

c. $\frac{1}{3}$, $\frac{3}{6}$, $\frac{9}{12}$, ____, ____

Rule

Part 3

A $\dfrac{3}{2} = \dfrac{6}{4}$

B $\dfrac{1}{4} = \dfrac{3}{12}$

C $\dfrac{2}{5} = \dfrac{4}{10}$

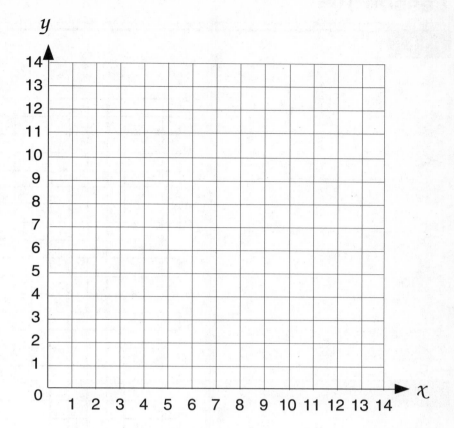

Lesson 106

a. _____

_____

b. _____

_____

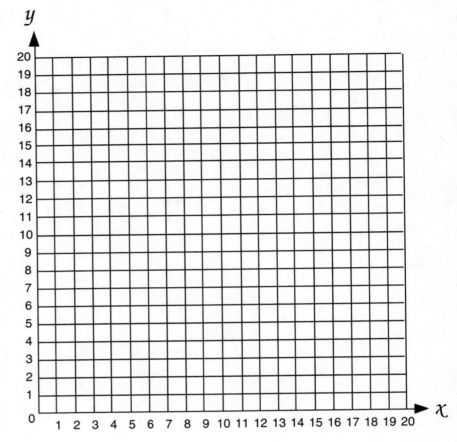